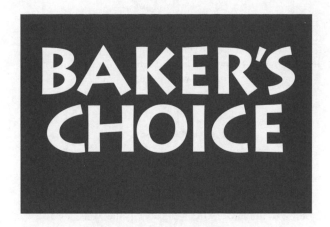

BAKER'S CHOICE

A Unit of High School Mathematics

INTERACTIVE
MATHEMATICS PROGRAM™

TEACHER'S GUIDE AND STUDENT BLACKLINE MASTERS

Dan Fendel and Diane Resek
with
Lynne Alper and Sherry Fraser

KEY CURRICULUM PRESS
Innovators in Mathematics Education

I M P

Authors
Dan Fendel and Diane Resek, San Francisco State University
with
Lynne Alper and Sherry Fraser, Teacher-Educators

Publisher
Steven Rasmussen

Project Editor
Casey FitzSimons

Additional Editorial
Dan Bennett, Bill Finzer, Greer Lleuad, Crystal Mills, Joe Todaro

Editorial Assistant
Caroline Ayres, Romy Snyder

Teacher Reviews
Dave Calhoun, Dwight Fuller, Rick Marks, Ph.D., Leslie Nielsen, Jim Short

Field Test Referrals
Sandie Gilliam, Toby Alexander

Cover and Design
Terry Lockman
Lumina Designworks

Cover Photography
Hilary Turner

Production
Luis Shein

Production Coordination
Susan Parini

Technical Graphics
Kirk Mills

Illustration
Martha Weston

This material is based upon work supported by the National Science Foundation
under award number ESI-9255262. Any opinions, findings, and conclusions or recommendations
expressed in this publication are those of the author(s) and do not necessarily reflect
the views of the National Science Foundation.

Key Curriculum Press
P.O. Box 2304
Berkeley, California 94702
510-548-2304
editorial@keypress.com

ISBN 1-55953-145-2
Printed in the United States of America

IMP Advisory Board Members

David Blackwell
Professor of Mathematics and Statistics
University of California, Berkeley
Berkeley, CA

Constance Clayton
Professor of Pediatrics
Chief Division of Community Health Care
Medical College of Pennsylvania
Philadelphia, PA

Tom Ferrio
Manager, Professional Calculators
Texas Instruments
Dallas, TX

Andrew M. Gleason
Hollis Professor of Mathematics and Natural Philosophy
Department of Mathematics
Harvard University
Cambridge, MA

Milton Gordon
President and Professor of Mathematics
California State University, Fullerton
Fullerton, CA

Shirley Hill
Curator's Professor of Education and Mathematics
School of Education, University of Missouri
Kansas City, MO

Steven Leinwand
Mathematics Consultant
Connecticut Department of Education
Hartford, CT

Art McArdle
Northern California Surveyors Apprentice Committee
Oakland, CA

Diane Ravitch (1994 only)
Brookings Institution
Washington, D.C.

Roy Romer (1992-1994 only)
Governor
State of Colorado
Denver, CO

Karen Sheingold
Research Director
Educational Testing Service
Princeton, NJ

Theodore R. Sizer
Chairman
Coalition of Essential Schools
Brown University
Providence, RI

Gary D. Watts
Educational Consultant
St. George, UT

Baker's Choice *Pilot Teachers*

Percy Chirinas
Santa Cruz High School
Santa Cruz, CA

Thom Dodd
Aptos High School
Aptos, CA

Emily Duffus
Harbor High School
Ben Lomond, CA

Kim Gough
San Lorenzo Valley High School
Felton, CA

Lori Green
Lincoln High School
Stockton, CA

Steve Hansen
Napa High School
Napa, CA

Tamara Jenkins
Soquel High School
Soquel, CA

Rob Lahey
San Lorenzo Valley High School
Felton, CA

Ernie Li
Mission High School
San Francisco, CA

Darryl Lykins
Lincoln High School
Stockton, CA

Melody Martinez
Rosemead High School
Rosemead, CA

Bill Medigovich
Redwood High School
Larkspur, CA

Leslie Robertson
West High School
Tracy, CA

Tom Schneider
Rosemead High School
Rosemead, CA

Jim Short
Hueneme High School
Oxnard, CA

Greg Smith
Tracy Joint Union High School
Tracy, CA

Sylvia Turner
Lincoln High School
Stockton, CA

Terry Umstead
San Lorenzo Valley High School
Felton, CA

Randy Vincent
Harbor High School
Ben Lomond, CA

IMP Teacher Advisory Group

Many teachers contributed enormously to the development of the IMP curriculum by using the materials in their classrooms and providing feedback to the project directors. Twelve schools were involved with IMP during the initial phase of the project, 1989–1992, and the teachers at these schools became IMP's Teacher Advisory Group. These teachers met with the IMP directors for a working retreat every spring from 1990 through 1995, and are listed here with the schools at which they taught during 1989–1992.

Dean Ballard
Mission High School, San Francisco, CA

Carolyn Barth
Tracy Joint Union High School, Tracy, CA

Larry Biggers
Highlands High School, San Antonio, TX

Libby Berry
Silver Creek High School, San Jose, CA

Matt Bremer
Berkeley High School, Berkeley, CA

Janice Bussey
Tracy Joint Union High School, Tracy, CA

Greg Cotton
Grant High School, Portland, OR

Margaret DeArmond
East Bakersfield High School, Bakersfield, CA

Sandy Douglass
Grant High School, Portland, OR

Eileen Favalora
Tracy Joint Union High School, Tracy, CA

Valorie Fayfich
Lanier High School, San Antonio, TX

Donna Gaarder
Tracy Joint Union High School, Tracy, CA

Lori Green
Tracy Joint Union High School, Tracy, CA

Philippe Henri
Berkeley High School, Berkeley, CA

Theresa Hernandez-Heinz
Mission High School, San Francisco, CA

Byron Hildebrand
Highlands High School, San Antonio, TX

Steve Jenkins
Eaglecrest High School, Aurora, CO

Dan Johnson
Silver Creek High School, San Jose, CA

George Kirchner
Tracy Joint Union High School, Tracy, CA

Jean Klanica
Eaglecrest High School, Aurora, CO

Barbara Knox
Grant High School, Portland, OR

Jim Luhring
Eaglecrest High School, Aurora, CO

Susan Malberg
Berkeley High School, Berkeley, CA

Tony Mana
Mission High School, San Francisco, CA

Leigh Ann McCready
Live Oak High School, Morgan Hill, CA

Reuben Miller
Beacon High School, Oakland, CA

Fred Rectanus
Grant High School, Portland, OR

Robin Rice
Tyee High School, Seattle, WA

Dennis Ross
Mission High School, San Francisco, CA

Barbara Schallau
Silver Creek High School, San Jose, CA

Linda Schroers
Tracy Joint Union High School, Tracy, CA

Frank Slaton
Silver Creek High School, San Jose, CA

Greg Smith
Tracy Joint Union High School, Tracy, CA

Nancy Springer
Beacon High School, Oakland, CA

Cathie Thompson
East Bakersfield High School, Bakersfield, CA

Becky Troutman
Tracy Joint Union High School, Tracy, CA

Jim Tucker
Grant High School, Portland, OR

Kathryn Wallentine
Tyee High School, Seattle, WA

Jack Withrow
Tyee High School, Seattle, WA

Margaret Wong
Berkeley High School, Berkeley, CA

Judy Wright
Lanier High School, San Antonio, TX

Sue Yabuki
Grant High School, Portland, OR

Adrienne Yank
Berkeley High School, Berkeley, CA

Tom Zimmerman
Mission High School, San Francisco, CA

Baker's Choice

Special Acknowledgments

Although many people contributed to the development of *Baker's Choice,* the IMP directors especially want to acknowledge Matt Bremer, who has worked on the revisions of the entire IMP curriculum, including the unit *Cookies* from which *Baker's Choice* was adapted; Mary Jo Cittadino, who became a high school student once again during the piloting of Years 1–3 of the curriculum and has answered thousands of questions from parents, teachers, and administrators; Lori Green, who as National Teaching Coordinator for IMP has seen more classes using the curriculum than we can count and who worked on the adaptation of *Cookies;* Celia Stevenson, whose graphics for *Cookies* served as the inspiration for much of the art in *Baker's Choice;* and the staff members at the National IMP office whose hard work and dedication is greatly appreciated: Barbara Ford, Tony Gillies, Marianne Smith, and Linda Witnov.

Dan Fendel

Diane Resek

Lynne Alper

Sherry Fraser

What is Baker's Choice?

Baker's Choice is a transition unit of high school mathematics from the Interactive Mathematics Program (IMP). We designed it to exemplify the curriculum reform called for in the *Curriculum and Evaluation Standards* of the National Council of Teachers of Mathematics.

What is a "transition unit of high school mathematics"?

You may want to teach a curriculum in the spirit of the *Standards* and to have your students learn in new ways. If you find it impractical right now to implement such a curriculum for the entire year, *Baker's Choice* provides you with a transitional step in this process of change, allowing you to incorporate a new experience into your regular program. If you undertake the teaching of *Baker's Choice,* we strongly recommend you do so along with a colleague at your own school, someone with whom you can meet and talk through your daily experiences.

What is the Interactive Mathematics Program (IMP)?

The Interactive Mathematics Program (IMP) is a collaboration of mathematicians, teacher-educators, and teachers who have been working together since 1989 on both curriculum development and teacher professional development. IMP has created a four-year program of problem-based mathematics which replaces the traditional Algebra I–Geometry–Algebra II/Trigonometry–Precalculus sequence. The IMP curriculum is designed around problem-centered units, and integrates traditional areas of mathematics with new topics such as statistics, probability, curve-fitting, and matrix algebra. Although each IMP unit has a specific mathematical focus (for instance, similar triangles), the unit is structured around its central problem and brings in other topics as needed, rather than narrowly restricting the mathematical content. Ideas that are developed initially in one unit are generally revisited and deepened in one or more later units.

For which students is IMP intended?

IMP is for all students. One of IMP's goals is to make the learning of a core mathematics curriculum accessible to everyone. Toward that end, we have designed the program for use with heterogeneous classes. We provide you with a varied collection of supplemental problems to give you flexibility to meet individual student needs.

How is the IMP classroom different?

Your role as a teacher changes from "imparter of knowledge" to observer and facilitator. You ask challenging questions. You do not give all the answers but you prod students to do their own thinking, to make generalizations, and to go beyond the immediate problem by asking themselves "What if?" The IMP curriculum gives students many opportunities to write about their mathematical thinking, to reflect on what they have done, and to make oral presentations to each other about their work. Your assessment of students becomes integrated with learning in IMP, and you evaluate students according to a variety of criteria, including class participation, daily homework assignments, Problems of the Week (POWs), portfolios, and unit assessments.

Contents

About This Guide

This is not an ordinary teacher's guide. Instead, it is a professional development manual to accompany a new approach to mathematics education. The guide is intended to supplement appropriate inservice support.

The general structure of the guide is a day-by-day description of how to teach the unit, somewhat like a very complete set of daily lesson plans. Overall, the guide describes the sequence and context in which mathematical ideas are introduced, and contains the specific activities and problems through which students will learn.

The notes for each day contain most of the following:

- A brief outline showing the mathematical topics, the additional materials needed, and the activities planned for that day

- A fairly detailed discussion of how the mathematical ideas should evolve from the activities and discussions

- Further material for teachers on the mathematical ideas, including:

  Suggestions of hints to give or questions to ask to promote student dialogue

  As a convenience, some of the equations, graphs, and numerical answers that make up the solutions to the problems

  Additional mathematical background

- Comments about the level of understanding to be expected from students at each stage of the unit's development

- Suggestions about the pedagogical format of each part of the day's lesson—for instance, when to use groups, how to choose presenters, and so on.

The suggestions throughout this guide are mostly just that—suggestions. As you work through this unit, you will constantly be called upon to exercise your professional expertise about how to proceed, what to expect, what approaches to use, and so on. Although this guide contains many ideas and suggestions, it is not a replacement for the on-site, on-the-spot judgment calls of the individual teacher for the individual classroom. We wish you well in this adventure!

• *Finding what you need*

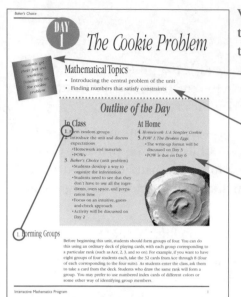

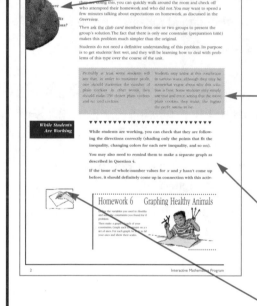

We designed this guide to help you find what you need amid all of this information. Each of the following components has a special treatment in the layout of the guide:

Synopsis of the day: The key idea or activity for each day is summarized in a brief sentence or two.

Mathematical Topics: Mathematical issues for the day are presented in a bulleted list.

Outline of the Day: The outline summarizes the *In Class* and *At Home* activities and topics for the day. These are keyed to numbered headings in the discussion.

Suggested questions: These are specific questions that you might ask during an activity or discussion to promote student insight or to determine whether students understand an idea. The appropriateness of these questions generally depends on what students have already developed or presented on their own.

Asides: These are ideas outside the main thrust of a discussion. They include background information for teachers, refinements or subtle points that may only be of interest to some students, ways to help fill in gaps in understanding the main ideas, and suggestions about when to bring in a particular concept.

While students are working: These notes suggest ways you can support students while groups work on particular in-class activities. They include things to watch for, questions you can ask, or examples to propose.

Icons for student written products: For each group activity, there is an icon suggesting a single group report, individual reports, or no report at all. If graphs are included, the icon indicates this as well.

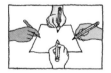

Single group report

Individual reports

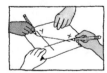

Single group graph

Individual graphs

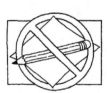

No report at all

Overview of Baker's Choice

• *Summary of the Unit*

The focus of this unit is using graphs of linear equations and inequalities to understand and solve problems. Although the central problem of the unit is a linear programming problem, it is not the goal of the unit to have students learn an algorithm for solving such problems (for instance, "the solution is always at a corner"). Rather, the goals are for students to deepen their understanding of the relationship between equations or inequalities and their graphs and for them to reason and solve problems using graphs.

Students begin by considering a typical linear programming problem—to maximize the profit of a bakery that makes plain and iced cookies. The situation is constrained by the amount of cookie dough and icing the bakery has on hand and the amount of oven time and labor time available. Each of these constraints represents a linear inequality affecting the number of cookies of each type to be made. The profit is a linear function of these numbers of cookies.

Students work toward a graphical solution of the problem. They begin with an intuitive investigation of linear inequalities and their graphs, leading to the recognition that the graph of a linear inequality in two variables is a half plane, bounded by the graph of the related linear equation.

Next, they combine the linear inequalities that represent constraints in the unit problem. They see that the ordered pairs representing the number of plain cookies and the number of iced cookies must be inside or on the boundary of a polygonal region in the coordinate plane. This region is called the **feasible region** for the set of constraints. Students realize that their goal is to find the point or points in this region where the linear profit function has its maximum value.

Then they leave the cookie problem for a while, and work on problems with fewer constraints. They study the linear profit function (or its analogue) by looking at the points where this linear function (in two variables) has a particular fixed value. They discover that, for any fixed value of the function, these points lie on a straight line, often called a **profit line** and, that as the fixed value of the function changes, the line moves in a parallel manner.

From this idea of a family of parallel profit lines, students conclude that to maximize the linear function, they need the line in the family that intersects their feasible region at some extreme. They see that such an extreme must be the point of intersection of two lines defining the boundary of the feasible region.

Students explore these general ideas through a variety of problem settings, including an artist deciding what type of pictures to paint, a pet owner choosing food for his pet, and a university deciding how many in-state and how many out-of-state students to admit.

With their experience with such problems in hand, students return to solve the original cookie problem. They must present a clear explanation of how they know that their solution does maximize profit.

The daily organization of the unit and some of the main activities can be summarized as follows:

- Days 1–2: Introduction of the central unit problem, *Baker's Choice;* expressing constraints symbolically

- Day 3: *Investigating Inequalities,* exploring equivalent inequalities

- Days 4–5: *Picturing Cookies—Part I,* finding the graphs of linear inequalities

- Day 6: Presentations of *POW 1: The Broken Eggs*

- Days 7–8: *Picturing Cookies—Part II*, combining graphs of linear inequalities to form a feasible region

- Days 9–10: *Profitable Pictures,* exploring the idea of a family of parallel profit lines

- Day 11: Presentations of *POW 2: Kick It!*

- Day 12: *Rock 'n' Rap,* another problem involving a family of parallel profit lines

- Day 13 (optional): Solving equations for one variable in terms of another and using a graphing calculator to solve *Rock 'n' Rap*

- Days 14–15: Returning to the central unit problem and its solution and explanation using graphs

- Days 16–18: *Portfolios,* end-of-unit assessments, summing up

• *Assumptions*

You can use *Baker's Choice* toward the end of a traditional Algebra I course or at any later point in a traditional high school sequence.

The unit makes these assumptions about students' backgrounds:

- Students have a general familiarity with the concept of the graph of an equation.

- Students have some experience graphing linear equations.

- Students know at least one method for solving pairs of linear equations in two variables.

However, the unit does not assume fluency or mastery of these ideas. Time is spent allowing students to work with these ideas intuitively and develop their own approaches to them. For example, students can use graphical methods as well as formal algebraic approaches to solve systems of equations.

The level of the class you teach will affect the pace and depth of students' work, and students in more advanced classes may be able to omit some activities (for instance, *Investigating Inequalities* on Day 3 or *Homework 13: The Big U*).

• Concepts and Skills

Listed here are the main concepts and skills that students will encounter during the course of this unit. Students will:

- Express and interpret constraints using inequalities.

- Graph individual linear inequalities and systems of linear inequalities.

- See that setting a linear expression equal to different constants gives a family of parallel lines.

- Find the maximum of a linear function over a polygonal region.

- Relate the idea of intersection of graphs to the idea of common solution of equations.

- Examine how the parameters in a problem can affect the nature of the solutions.

- Solve linear equations for one variable in terms of another.

- Use graphing calculators to draw feasible regions.

- Use graphing calculators to estimate points of intersection of graphs.

- Combine various concepts and skills listed above to solve linear programming problems with two variables.

Other topics are explored through the two Problems of the Week (POWs), which are essentially independent of the rest of the unit.

• Group Work

In-class activities of the unit are designed for students working together in small groups, preferably of four students each. On Day 1 we describe a procedure for forming random groups. We recommend that you form new groups on Day 6 and on Day 11.

• Reading and ESL Students

This unit requires more student reading than a traditional mathematics text. If you have students for whom English is not a first language or other students who might have reading difficulties, you should pay attention to their needs for support in connection with the reading of problems. Some students will need help understanding puns, colloquial humor, and situations unique to American culture.

• *Calculators*

We strongly recommend that each classroom have a class set of graphing calculators, out and readily available to students at all times during class.

If graphing calculators are not available, students should at least have ordinary calculators within arm's reach, both in class and at home. Students should be able to use this tool as they would use pencil and paper—spontaneously and flexibly. This unit includes an optional activity that focuses specifically on graphing calculator use, but use of calculators should not be limited to this day.

• *Portfolios*

A mathematics portfolio is a way for students to share their writings, experiences, knowledge, interests, concerns, and expertise. People outside the classroom can sense what is valued in mathematics by reading a student portfolio. Students in the classroom benefit from reading and sharing each other's work.

In this unit, students learn mathematics in a variety of contexts—through classwork, homework assignments, Problems of the Week (POWs), presentations to small groups and to the class, and end-of-unit assessments. At the end of the unit, they select specific samples of their work and incorporate them into a portfolio. Written explanations for their selections are part of a cover letter on their overall experience with the unit.

• *Time Span*

The material in this unit is planned to encompass about three weeks of instruction time (15 class periods), with an additional three days planned for portfolio compilation, assessment, and final summary of the unit.

However, you may find that your own experience is different. Some activities (for instance, *Investigating Inequalities* on Day 3) may cover ideas familiar to your students, and you may choose to shorten or omit them. On the other hand, you may find that it takes your class longer as you encounter difficult concepts or as students go further than anticipated with certain activities.

You should not expect every student to master every concept when first encountered. Students will likely have more opportunities to work with the concept in this unit and elsewhere. On the other hand, if most of the class is confused on a major point, you may decide to spend extra time on it.

• *Home Assignments*

Students have two types of assignments outside of class—daily homework and Problems of the Week (POWs).

• *Daily Homework*

This guide contains daily homework assignments. They form an important part of the learning process.

To encourage students to prepare their homework assignments before coming to class, you can check off which students have (or have not) done their assignments as you circulate through the room at the beginning of class. If the students will not need their homework during the class discussion, then you can collect homework as students enter the room (but see suggestions below on grading).

It is worthwhile discussing your expectations concerning homework. You can tell students that, if they don't know how to do a particular assignment, they should contact someone from their group.

If they still have trouble, you can have them write about their difficulties, indicating what part of the assignment they understand and what they don't understand, and describing the efforts they have made. In this way, they will always be able to hand in something, and "I didn't know how to do it" will not be a legitimate excuse for not turning in an assignment.

• *Problems of the Week*

This unit contains two Problems of the Week (POWs)—open-ended problems that are not tied to the main ideas of the unit.

Both of these problems should be immediately accessible to all students, but they also provide room for students to go into as much depth as they wish. The POWs give students experience with an exploratory approach to mathematics and give them some insight into the process of how they learn.

Since these problems are outside the main stream of the curriculum, they may provide a real challenge to you as well. Try to view them as an opportunity to work with your students as a team, rather than as an area where you need to be the expert.

This teacher's guide suggests that you give students a week for each of these problems, in part, because they do not lend themselves to any fixed algorithm or approach. Students may need to work on the problems at several sittings before their ideas coalesce.

The week of work allows students to examine their process in working on a mathematics problem and to write about that experience. Thus, you expect them to show their reasoning in more detail than on a daily homework assignment. Each POW is accompanied by guidelines for the student write-ups.

• *Materials*

You will need the following materials throughout this unit (in addition to standard materials such as transparencies, chart paper, and marking pens):

- Graphing calculators (strongly recommended; one per student is desirable)

- Grid chart paper

- Graph paper

- Graph paper transparencies

- Rulers

- Colored pencils (for use in case students forget to bring them)

- A deck of cards or colored index cards (for forming random groups)

In addition to these regular materials, you will probably want, for Day 10, an overhead transparency of the feasible region found in the Day 9 discussion of *Homework 8: Picturing Pictures.* Also, you will need to reproduce the in-class and take-home unit assessments for use on Day 17.

Students need to provide the following:

- Scientific calculators for use at home (and at school if no calculators are provided).

- Graph paper for use at home.

- Colored pencils in four different colors.

• *Grading*

Although you will probably want to check daily that students have done their homework, and include regularity of homework completion as part of students' grades, you will probably not be able to read thoroughly every assignment that they turn in.

Therefore, you will need to select certain assignments to read carefully and to grade. You may want to alert students that you will give special importance to particular projects in terms of grading.

We recommend the following homework and class activities as tools for grading, in addition to the end-of-unit assessments (in-class and take-home), the POWs, and the unit portfolio:

- *Homework 3: Variables of Your Own*

- *Picturing Cookies—Part II* (Days 7–8 activity)

- *Homework 11: Changing What You Eat*

- *Baker's Choice Revisited* (Days 14–15 activity)

If you want to base your grading on more tasks, there are many other homework assignments, class activities, and oral presentations you can use.

DAY 1

The Cookie Problem

> *Students get their feet wet working intuitively on the cookie problem*

Mathematical Topics

- Introducing the central problem of the unit
- Finding numbers that satisfy constraints

Outline of the Day

In Class

1. Form random groups
2. Introduce the unit and discuss expectations
   - Homework and materials
   - POWs
3. *Baker's Choice* (unit problem)
   - Students develop a way to organize the information
   - Students need to see that they don't have to use all the ingredients, oven space, and preparation time
   - Focus on an intuitive, guess-and-check approach
   - Activity will be discussed on Day 2

At Home

4. *Homework 1: A Simpler Cookie*
5. *POW 1: The Broken Eggs*
   - The write-up format will be discussed on Day 3
   - POW is due on Day 6

1. Forming Groups

Before beginning this unit, students should form groups of four. You can do this using an ordinary deck of playing cards, with each group corresponding to a particular rank (such as Ace, 2, 3, and so on). For example, if you want to have eight groups of four students each, take the 32 cards from Ace through 8 (four of each corresponding to the four suits). As students enter the class, ask them to take a card from the deck. Students who draw the same rank will form a group. You may prefer to use numbered index cards of different colors or some other way of identifying group members.

(*Note:* IMP strongly recommends that groups be formed randomly using a method like the ones described above. If you contrive to put a mix of abilities in every group, students often decide what their assigned roles are and act to fulfill them. In randomly created groups, students feel as if they can make a new beginning with each group change. This is especially important as students undertake this unit using what may be for them a new approach to doing mathematics.)

Students should write down which suit and rank they receive, since this guide often suggests choosing students for presentations on the basis of these suits. In this way, all students will have the opportunity and responsibility to represent their group. You can pass around a sheet on which students record their rank and suit, so that you will have that sheet to refer to later in case students forget their suits or ranks.

Suggest to students that they exchange phone numbers with group members. That will allow them to contact each other to discuss mathematical ideas or to find out what they missed if they were absent. Stress that, if they are absent or do not understand an assignment, they should not wait until they come back to class to get their questions answered—they should call a group member. Fellow students are a great resource that they are expected to utilize.

We recommend that you form new groups on Day 6 and Day 11.

2. Introduction to an IMP Unit

Since this unit is a departure from the students' regular textbook, you should spend a few minutes going over some of the basics. In particular, you will probably want to talk with students about what outside work will be expected from them. You may also want to talk about the overall philosophy of the unit, especially its use of a central problem as the vehicle for the development of new ideas.

•*Homework and materials*

Tell students that, in this unit, homework is required each and every night (in addition to work on their POW). If they cannot do the homework, they should consult with a group member. If they still cannot do the homework, they should write about what they tried, what they didn't understand, what didn't work, and so on.

Also, tell students to bring colored pencils (at least four different colors) for use beginning tomorrow. They will need them occasionally throughout the unit.

•*Problems of the Week*

(You may want to review for yourself the rationale for POWs given in the overview of this unit. You can either discuss POWs as part of the general introduction to the unit or allow some time at the end of today to introduce the first POW.)

Tell students that, in addition to homework each night, they will be working on a POW. *Note:* Although the unit is about 3 weeks long, it contains only two POWs.

Tell students that working on POWs will help them become independent problem solvers and independent learners of mathematics. Also tell them that "real" problems take more than 10 minutes to solve and are best solved over time. Coming back to a problem on several occasions is especially helpful if one gets nowhere at first.

Emphasize to students that it will be difficult to solve the problem and do a good write-up the night before the problem is due, so they should do some work on these problems every day.

3. *Baker's Choice*

Reminder: Be sure that calculators are within reach of every student. It is important that students be able to focus on the mathematical ideas of the unit rather than get bogged down in arithmetic.

Have students read the unit's main problem, which has the same name as the unit, *Baker's Choice.* You may wish to have several students take turns reading portions of it aloud. Then let them work in groups on the questions in the activity.

The situation described in this activity will often be referred to in these notes as "the unit problem."

The activity will be discussed tomorrow, and students should save their notes for that discussion.

As students work today, you can give several groups overhead transparencies to use in preparing presentations of their results for tomorrow's discussion. Look for groups that organized the information in different ways.

**While Students
Are Working**

▼ ▼

Part of the difficulty of this problem is keeping track of all the numbers. Be sure to let students develop their own way of organizing the information, since this is a valuable skill, both in life and in mathematics. Although it may require more class time for students to do this on their own, that time is extremely worthwhile.

As you observe the groups at work, make sure that students realize that the numbers they are looking for are in *dozens* of each kind. For example, they should give answers such as "4 dozen plain, 3 dozen iced," not "48 plain, 36 iced."

Students may have trouble at first because they think that they have to make use of all the ingredients, all the oven space, and all the preparation time available. Let them realize on their own that this is impossible and also see that it is not required by the problem.

Possible hint: "Is it possible for the Woos to make 1 dozen of each kind? 3 dozen iced and 5 dozen plain?" and so on.

If they seem stuck, ask them if it's possible for the Woos to make 1 dozen of each kind, or 3 dozen plain and 5 dozen iced, and so

on. In other words, urge them to use a guess-and-check approach in their groups. Do not push them to think about the problem in any different or "better" way. You want to encourage independent problem solving.

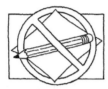

Student book page 1 →

Baker's Choice

Abby and Bing Woo have a small bakery shop that specializes in cookies.

They make only two kinds of cookies—plain cookies and cookies with icing. They need to decide *how many dozens* of each kind of cookies to make for tomorrow.

One dozen of their *plain* cookies requires a pound of cookie dough (and no icing), while one dozen of their *iced* cookies requires 0.7 pounds of cookie dough and 0.4 pounds of icing.

The Woos know from experience that each dozen of the plain cookies requires about 0.1 hours of preparation time, and each dozen of the iced cookies requires about 0.15 hours of preparation time.

They also know that, no matter how many of each kind they make, they will be able to sell them all.

Their decision is limited by the following things:

• The ingredients they have on hand—they have 110 pounds of cookie dough and 32 pounds of icing.

• The amount of oven space available—they have room to bake a total of 140 dozen cookies for tomorrow.

• The amount of preparation time available—together they have 15 hours for cookie preparation.

Why on earth should the Woos care how many cookies of each kind they make? Well, you guessed it! They want to make as much money as possible. They sell the plain cookies for $6.00 a dozen and it costs them $4.50 a dozen to make those cookies. The iced cookies sell for $7.00 a dozen and cost $5.00 a dozen to make.

The Big Question is:

How many dozens of each kind of cookie should Abby and Bing make so that their profit is as high as possible?

1. a. To begin answering the Big Question, find one combination of plain cookies and iced cookies that will satisfy all of the conditions in the problem.

   b. Find out how much profit the Woos will make on that combination of cookies.

2. Now find a different combination of cookies that fits the problem, but that makes a greater profit for the Woos.

This problem was adapted from one in *Introduction to Linear Programming,* 2nd Edition, by R. Stansbury Stockton, Allyn and Bacon, 1963, pp. 19–35.

4. *Homework 1: A Simpler Cookie*

This homework looks at a simpler version of the Woos' cookie problem. You can remind students that simplifications are often helpful in mathematics in seeing how to attack a particular type of problem.

Student book page 2 →

Homework 1   A Simpler Cookie

The Woos have a rather complicated problem to solve. Let's make it simpler. Finding a solution to a simpler problem may lead to a method for solving the original problem.

Assume that the Woos still make plain cookies and cookies with icing. Also assume that they still have 15 hours altogether for cookie preparation.

But now assume that they have an unlimited amount of both cookie dough and icing and that they have an unlimited amount of space in their oven.

The other information is unchanged, and is as follows:

- Preparing a dozen plain cookies requires 0.1 hours.
- Preparing a dozen iced cookies requires 0.15 hours.
- They sell the plain cookies for $6.00 a dozen.
- It costs them $4.50 a dozen to make plain cookies.
- They sell the iced cookies for $7.00 a dozen.
- It costs them $5.00 a dozen to make iced cookies.

As before, the Woos know that no matter how many of each kind they make, they will be able to sell them all.

1. Find at least five combinations of plain and of iced cookies that the Woos could make without working more than 15 hours. For each combination, find the profit that they would make.

2. Find the combination of plain and iced cookies that you think would give the Woos the greatest profit. Explain why you think no other combination will give a greater profit.

Amber Conover and Anandika Muni discuss homework results in their group.

5. POW 1: The Broken Eggs

Tell students you will be discussing what is needed for the write-up in more detail later (see Day 3), but that they need to keep their scratch paper or notes as they work on this problem, since they will be expected to write a description of how they worked toward a solution.

You need not go over the problem itself today, since students will have a chance on Day 3 to discuss their progress. However, if you feel that you need to introduce the ideas of POWs to your students, and you are short of time today, you can delay introduction of the POW until Day 2.

This POW is scheduled for discussion on Day 6.

Student book page 3 →

POW 1   The Broken Eggs

A farmer is taking her eggs to market in her cart, but she hits a pot-hole, which knocks over all the containers of eggs.

Though she herself is unhurt, every egg is broken.

So she goes to her insurance agent, who asks her how many eggs she had. She says she doesn't know, but she remembers some things from various ways she tried packing the eggs.

She knows that when she put the eggs in groups of two, there was one egg left over. When she put them in groups of three, there was also one egg left over. The same thing happened when she put them in groups of four, groups of five, or groups of six.

But when she put them in groups of seven, she ended up with complete groups of seven with no eggs left over.

Your task is to answer the following question:

What can the farmer figure out from this information about how many eggs she had? Is there more than one possibility?

Write-up

You should write up your work on this problem using the following categories:

1. **Process:** Based on your notes, describe what you did in attempting to solve this problem. You might want to talk about such things as approaches you tried that didn't work, what you did when you got stuck, who you talked to and any ideas you got from them, and so on.

2. **Results:**

   a. State your results on the problem as clearly as you can. (If you only obtained a partial solution, give that.) Include any insights you had other than numerical solutions.

   b. Explain how you know that your answer (or partial answer) is correct. Your explanation should be written in a way that will be convincing to someone else—even someone who initially disagrees with your answer.

DAY 2

The Constraints

The conditions of the unit problem are put into algebraic form.

Mathematical Topics

- Finding numbers that satisfy constraints
- Maximizing profit
- Expressing constraints as inequalities

Outline of the Day

Note: Be sure to leave approximately 10 minutes at the end of class to introduce tonight's homework.

In Class

1. Discuss *Homework 1: A Simpler Cookie*
   - Maximize profit in this situation by maximizing the number of plain cookies

2. Discuss *Baker's Choice* (activity from Day 1)
   - Students present their organizational schemes
   - Introduce the term **constraint**
   - Ask how and when to compute profit
   - Ask for combinations that do not satisfy the constraints

3. Discuss the constraints as inequalities, both verbally and symbolically
   - Post the constraints for later reference

$$x + 0.7y \leq 110 \quad \text{(cookie dough)}$$
$$0.4y \leq 32 \quad \text{(icing)}$$
$$x + y \leq 140 \quad \text{(oven space)}$$
$$0.1x + 0.15y \leq 15 \quad \text{(prep time)}$$

   - Other constraints ($x \geq 0$ and $y \geq 0$) can be added later (see Day 7)
   - Develop the profit expression $1.5x + 2y$

4. Restrictions on x and y (optional for today—see also Day 7)
   - x and y cannot be negative
   - x and y must be integers

At Home

5. *Homework 2: High School Letters*
   - Discuss the term **summary phrase**
   - If necessary, introduce subscripts

1. Discussion of
Homework 1:
A Simpler Cookie

Ask students to discuss their homework solutions briefly in groups. While they are doing this, you can quickly walk around the room and check off who attempted their homework and who did not. You may want to spend a few minutes talking about expectations on homework, as discussed in the *Overview.*

Then ask the *club card* members from one or two groups to present the group's solution. The fact that there is only one constraint (preparation time) makes this problem much simpler than the original.

Students do not need a definitive understanding of this problem. Its purpose is to get students' feet wet, and they will be learning how to deal with problems of this type over the course of the unit.

The discussion itself should help students begin to share their own thoughts, to listen to others, to learn to ask questions of each other when they don't understand, and to politely disagree if they think someone's reasoning doesn't make sense.

Probably at least some students will see that, in order to maximize profit, one should maximize the number of plain cookies. In other words, they should make 150 dozen plain cookies and no iced cookies.

Students may arrive at this conclusion in various ways, although they may be somewhat vague about why this solution is best. Some students may simply use trial and error, seeing that the more plain cookies they make, the higher the profit seems to be.

2. Discussion of
Baker's Choice

You can begin the discussion with presentations from the groups to which you gave overhead transparencies yesterday. You might have the *diamond card* members of these groups present their organizational schemes for keeping track of the various conditions and deciding what profit would result from different cookie combinations.

Then have *diamond card* members of other groups offer other combinations of cookies that they think are possible. You can use one of the schemes presented, or a blend of them that the class develops, to keep track of students' suggestions.

"Are you sure that this combination fits all the conditions? How do you know?"

As combinations are offered, ask students to check to see if the combinations satisfy the conditions by calculating the amount of cookie dough, icing, oven space, and preparation time required for each combination, and determining if the results are within the conditions of the problem.

Introduce the word **constraint** in this context as a synonym for *condition* (especially in the sense of *restrictive* condition).

Ask students how and when to compute the profit for each combination. They may see that it makes sense to wait until they see if a combination fits all the constraints before they make the calculation. Leave them in charge of the process as much as possible.

"What's an example of a combination that does not fit all the constraints?"

Ask groups for a combination they tried which *did not* satisfy the constraints, and have them explain which constraint or constraints the combination failed to satisfy. It is just as important for students to see why a combination is excluded as it is for them to show that it is included. It is also important that students see that each condition is a separate constraint and that a combination must satisfy all four constraints.

Do enough of these combinations to develop a clear method for working with them. You do not need to look at all the combinations that students suggest.

3. Constraints as Inequalities

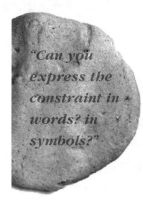

"Can you express the constraint in words? in symbols?"

Pick one of the conditions to focus on, such as the amount of cookie dough available, and ask students to explain how they decided whether a combination they tried did or did not satisfy this constraint.

Some students may be more comfortable with verbal statements, while others prefer to express the constraint symbolically.

A verbal statement might go something like this:

> "You take the number of dozens of iced cookies, multiply that by 0.7 and add the number of dozens of plain cookies, and you can't get more than 110."

Students who prefer a symbolic expression of the constraint will need to choose variables to represent "number of dozens of plain cookies" and "number of dozens of iced cookies." We will use x and y, respectively, for these two variables, so the constraint can be expressed by an inequality equivalent to $x + 0.7y \leq 110$.

It is important that all students be able to deal with both ways of expressing the condition. You may want to randomly ask some students for verbal expressions and others for symbolic expressions.

Proceed similarly with the other conditions. The class should end up with a set of constraint inequalities that looks something like this:

$$x + 0.7y \leq 110 \quad \text{(for the amount of cookie dough)}$$

$$0.4y \leq 32 \quad \text{(for the amount of icing)}$$

$$x + y \leq 140 \quad \text{(for the amount of oven space)}$$

$$0.1x + 0.15y \leq 15 \quad \text{(for the amount of the Woos' preparation time)}$$

Have students put these constraint inequalities on chart paper, and post this constraint chart for later use, perhaps labeling the chart "Cookies Constraints."

Point out that each constraint is represented symbolically by an **inequality**. Use the inequalities to check that the combinations used earlier really do satisfy the constraints. This will repeat their earlier computations, but it should be done at least once to confirm that the symbolic inequalities say the same thing as the verbal expression of these conditions.

• *The profit expression*

"What expression will give you the profit for a given combination?"

Ask students to develop an algebraic expression for the profit. If they have difficulty with this, have them go back to the chart in which they computed profit for various combinations. They should get the expression $1.5x + 2y$.

Students often make the mistake of treating the expression for the profit as another constraint. You may want to ask why this wasn't included in the earlier list of constraints in order to get a student to explain to the class why the profit expression is not a constraint.

As needed, bring out the difference between an *expression,* such as $1.5x + 2y$, and a *condition* or *constraint,* such as $x + 0.7y \leq 110$, which is a statement *about* an expression.

4. Restrictions on x and y

Because of the problem context from which the variables come, it makes sense to insist that x and y be whole numbers.

This issue is important, and definitely should be discussed now *if introduced by a student.* However, we recommend that, unless a student brings it up, you ignore it for now. The discussion will be more engaging and meaningful to students if it comes initially from them or arises in the natural context of discussing graphs or feasible regions later in the unit. The unit provides an opportunity for discussing restrictions on the variables in different contexts on Day 7.

If this issue does come up now, you can use the following ideas.

• *Two aspects to the restrictions issue*

There are actually two separate issues here: 1) that x and y cannot be negative, and 2) that x and y must be integers. (Actually, allowing x and y to be multiples of 1/12 would also make sense). It turns out that there is a simple fix for the first of these issues but not for the second.

If either one of these issues is raised, we suggest that you broaden the scope of the discussion to include both, perhaps asking students if there are other restrictions on the "eligible" values for x and y.

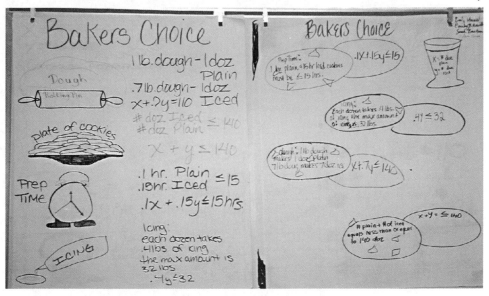

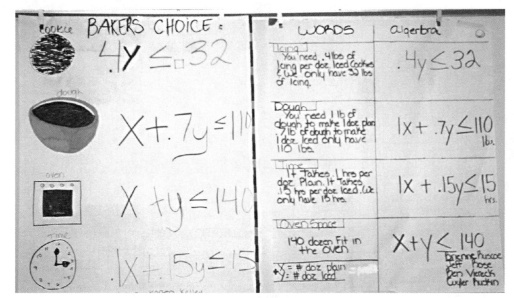

Allowing students to organize information in their own way is a first step in problem-solving. Four student groups created four different charts in Kim Gough's class at San Lorenzo Valley High School in Felton, California.

You can point out that the question of eligibility will depend on the particular problem situation. That is, negative or non-integer solutions will make sense in some problems but not in others.

• Avoiding negative values

Concerning the restriction to non-negative numbers, you can ask students if they can make this restriction using additional constraints. If a further hint is needed, you can ask if they can express the condition of "not being negative" as an inequality. They should see that the simple inequalities $x \geq 0$ and $y \geq 0$ will accomplish this.

In other words, adding these two constraints to the list fixes this aspect of the model. The class should include these inequalities on its posted constraint chart.

•*Avoiding non-integer values*

The problem of avoiding non-integer values is much more complex since it can not be handled by additional inequalities.

The best classroom approach for this difficulty probably is to tell students that there is no simple way to handle the issue and that they should ignore it for now. Emphasize that this means they will need to be especially careful to look at their solution and think whether it makes sense.

If it turns out that the solution that provides the maximum profit is somehow "ineligible," they will have to decide where to go from there. *Note:* It turns out in this problem that the combination with the maximum profit does have whole number values for x and y.

You can take this opportunity to talk about mathematical modeling. Bring out that we often need to make simplifications or ignore certain aspects of a problem in order to get a usable mathematical description. You can introduce the term **mathematical model** for this abstract description of the real-life situation.

Bring out that when simplifications are made it becomes especially important to check back into the actual problem after the mathematical analysis.

5. *Homework 2: High School Letters*

This homework is intended to start students thinking about how to use variables in meaningful ways.

If students are not familiar with the use of subscripts, take a minute to tell them that subscripted variables are used just as the single letters are—as abbreviations for lengthy expressions. Also explain how to read subscripted variables out loud. For example, say that we read G_9 as "G sub nine."

You can introduce the homework by restricting students' attention to the first nine variables. Ask whether someone can find a meaningful expression using them. If you get no response, ask what $G_9 + B_9$ stands for. Push for them to say "the number of 9th graders" rather than "the number of 9th grade girls plus the number of 9th grade boys." Tell them that the first phrase, "the number of 9th graders," is what is meant by a **summary phrase**.

Ask students for a few more examples. Use your judgment about how much of this type of preparation your students need. Keep in mind that they need not be experts on this, and that *Homework 3: Variables of Your Own* is a similar task.

*[Baker's Choice] seemed a lot more hands-on . . . .
[W]e got to draw our math and present it. It also
seemed a lot more meaningful this way because we
were working out problems not just for an answer, but
for a project and something that mattered.*

**Kate Thomas, Student
Homework 14: Reflections on Learning**

Student book page 4 →

Homework 2

High School Letters

The list below uses certain symbols or symbol combinations as variables to represent certain quantities concerning a particular high school.

For example, C stands for the number of classes each student takes at that high school; G_9 stands for the number of 9th grade girls at the school.

You may want to think of some of the numerical values as representing the average for the appropriate group of students.

symbol	meaning	numerical value
C	the number of classes taken by each student	5
G_9	the number of 9th grade girls	230
B_9	the number of 9th grade boys	246
G_{10}	the number of 10th grade girls	215
B_{10}	the number of 10th grade boys	213
G_{11}	the number of 11th grade girls	189
B_{11}	the number of 11th grade boys	198
G_{12}	the number of 12th grade girls	178
B_{12}	the number of 12th grade boys	183
H_M	the number of minutes each student spends on math homework each night	27
H_O	the number of minutes each student spends on homework other than math each night	52
M	the number of minutes each class lasts	50
D	the number of class days a year	180
L_G	the number of hours a week each girl student listens to music	18
L_B	the number of hours a week each boy student listens to music	15

Using the symbols above, it is possible to write many different algebraic expressions. Although you can always substitute numbers and do the arithmetic, most of these expressions have no real meaning in the situation.

For example, consider the expression DL_G. Certainly you can multiply "the number of class days a year" (180) by "the number of hours a week each girl student listens to music" (18), but the product

Continued on next page

Student book page 5 →

you get (3,240) doesn't have any interpretation in terms of the problem. In other words, DL_G doesn't really mean anything.

However, some expressions *do* have a meaning. For example, in the expression $H_M + H_O$, each term represents part of a student's homework time. The sum represents the total number of minutes each student spends on homework each night. So the expression $H_M + H_O$ is meaningful in the situation.

The phrase "the total number of minutes each student spends on homework each night" is a concise way to describe the number represented by $H_M + H_O$. We will call this concise description the **summary phrase** for the expression.

The list above tells us that each student spends 27 minutes on math homework, so $H_M = 27$, and that each student spends 52 minutes on other homework, so $H_O = 52$.

Therefore, $H_M + H_O = 27 + 52 = 79$, so each student spends 79 minutes a night on homework. But even if the numbers were different, $H_M + H_O$ would still represent the number of minutes each student spends on homework each night.

Your Task

Your task is to come up with as many *meaningful* algebraic expressions as you can, using the symbols above. For each expression, do each of the following:

- Write the expression.
- Explain what the expression means, using a summary phrase.
- Give the numerical value of the expression, based on the values of the individual variables given in the chart.

• • • • • • • • • • • • • •

DAY 3

Simplifying Inequalities

Students investigate whether methods for getting equivalent equations apply to inequalities.

Mathematical Topics

- Developing meaningful algebraic expressions
- Interpreting algebraic expressions in words using summary phrases
- Equivalent equations and inequalities

Outline of the Day

In Class

1. Discuss *Homework 2: High School Letters*
   - Work on summary phrases
2. Discuss progress on *POW 1: The Broken Eggs*
   - Components of the POW write-up
   - Collaboration versus copying
3. Introduce *Investigating Inequalities*
   - Review the term **equivalent**
   - Brainstorm on equivalent equations and the basics of inequalities
4. *Investigating Inequalities*
   - Students investigate how to get equivalent inequalities
5. Discuss *Investigating Inequalities*

- Focus on the case of multiplying by a negative number using the reflection model and an algebraic explanation based on addition
6. Simplifying the *Baker's Choice* inequalities

At Home

7. *Homework 3: Variables of Your Own*

1. Discussion of Homework 2: High School Letters

As you check off who did their homework, you can ask students to work in their groups to compile a list of meaningful expressions with their values.

Then ask the *heart card* member of each group to put one or two of the group's favorite expressions on the board or on chart paper, with the goal of trying to stump the other groups. (All groups can do this at the same time.)

Give the groups a few minutes to decide on the summary phrase for the expressions from the other groups.

You can then go around the room, one expression at a time, and let *spade card* members say what the summary phrase is, letting students look for ambiguities and fix them. (You do not need to do all of the expressions.)

This work may be difficult for your class, but tonight's homework will give them further opportunity to do similar work.

2. Reminder on POW 1: The Broken Eggs

"How is work going on your POWs?"

Ask students how work is progressing on the POW. Remind them that they should already have begun work on this problem, and that they need to leave time for preparing a good write-up.

Tell students that one goal of work on POWs is to get thoughtful, well-written work. That is why they are asked to work on it over a long period of time.

Give students an opportunity to ask any questions they have about the meaning of the problem, but try to limit any discussion of how to solve it. You may want to take a common mistaken answer such as 49 and ask someone to explain why the farmer couldn't have had that number of eggs.

"What should go into the Process section of the write-up? the Results section?"

• POW write-up

Ask students what they think should go into each part of the write-up. Use their ideas and suggestions to make your expectations clear. In particular, ask whether they think you should give much (or any) credit for a numerical answer without any explanation. You might also ask if they think a paper with an excellent discussion deserves a good grade even if it has a numerical error and so gets the wrong answer.

"Why is process an important part of the write-up?"

Continue the discussion by asking them why they think *process* is important. Try to have them understand that the main goal of the POW is for them to learn about how to solve new problems, and not to learn the answers to specific problems.

You may want to ask students who have already started work on the problem to give an idea of what one might say about the process. You might try asking questions such as, "What is one of the first things you learned about the number of eggs?" and "How did you realize that?"

• *Collaboration versus copying*

Use this time also as an opportunity to discuss the difference between working together and copying. The first is encouraged; the second is considered cheating, and is not allowed. Students should be able to offer good explanations of the differences. (For example, one generally learns from working with someone, but not from straight copying.)

Tell students that, if they work together on a POW, they should note this fact in the write-up. Assure them that there will be no downgrading of their work for this cooperative effort.

3. Introduction to *Investigating Inequalities*

Note: Although your students may already be familiar with rules for manipulating inequalities, they may benefit from this activity anyway, especially if you have them focus on explaining why the rules work. On the other hand, if they have previously shown substantial understanding of work with inequalities, you may decide to omit this activity, and just simplify the inequalities from the unit problem as a class. If students also did well on last night's homework, you may want to go straight to tomorrow's activity, *Picturing Cookies—Part I.*

In *Investigating Inequalities*, students will look at whether the techniques they know for getting equivalent equations will work for inequalities as well.

Before having students start this activity, you may want to brainstorm about equivalent equations. See the suggestions that follow. You may also want to consider the brief review of inequalities described under the subheading "Basics of inequalities."

However, your students may be able to go straight to the activity *Investigating Inequalities*. In that case, you can use the notes under "Introducing the activity" as the basis for the introduction.

• *Brainstorming about equivalent equations*

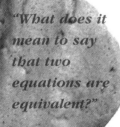

"*What does it mean to say that two equations are equivalent?*"

Ask students what it means to say that two equations are **equivalent**. If they do not know, tell them that two equations are called *equivalent* if they have the same solutions.

The term *equivalent* is a key one in mathematics, so be sure that students hear and use it properly in context. Nevertheless, the following discussion may go quickly. Even if students don't know the formal definition of *equivalent*, they probably are familiar with ways to get equivalent equations.

You can brainstorm with the class on this, perhaps starting with the equation $2x + 5 = 8$.

In other words, ask if they can find another equation which has the same solution as this one. If students don't come up with anything, you can ask leading questions such as, "What might you do to both sides?"

"How can you get another equation with the same solution as this one?" (If necessary: "What can you do to both sides?")

They will probably suggest subtracting 5 from both sides and then suggest dividing both sides by 2.

Use this example to confirm that the process gives equivalent equations. For instance, students may say that the equation above is equivalent to the equation $2x = 3$, and that this is equivalent to $x = 1.5$.

Have them verify that $x = 1.5$ does, in fact, solve each of the previous equations, so that all three equations are equivalent. You may want to point out that $x = 1.5$ is an equation just like the others; it has just been simplified to the point where it is obvious what the solution is.

You can bring out that this is a major purpose of working with equivalent equations—namely, to find something equivalent where the solution is obvious.

Based on this example (and others, if needed), have students generate a list of things that can be done to an equation that will produce an equivalent equation. They should come up with at least the following:

- Add the same number to both sides of the equality.

- Subtract the same number from both sides of the equality.

- Multiply both sides of the equality by the same non-zero number.

- Divide both sides of the equality by the same non-zero number.

You should bring out, if no student does, that in the last two items, "the same number" must be non-zero.

• *Basics of inequalities*

If your students have not worked recently with inequalities, you may want to do some brief background work on the meaning of inequalities.

For example, give them an inequality like $4x \leq 20$, and ask for values of x that fit this condition.

Use a number line to help students see what the set of numbers they are getting looks like. Be sure that they include fractions and negative numbers as well as whole numbers. Thus, they should see that the set of solutions to the inequality is the set of all points on the number line to the left of and including 5.

4. *Investigating Inequalities*

Tell students that their task in this activity is to investigate whether the techniques they use for getting equivalent *equations* can also be applied to *inequalities* to produce equivalent inequalities.

▼ ▼

As you circulate among groups while they work, check that they are using both positive and negative numbers in their investigations. If they are not, point this out to them and give them time within their groups to check if they have looked at all possibilities.

While Students Are Working

Student book page 6 →

Investigating Inequalities

You know that two equations are called **equivalent** if they have the same solutions. For example, the equation $2x + 5 = 8$ is equivalent to the equation $2x = 3$, since the equations have the same solution, $x = 1.5$.

You have also learned some techniques for creating equivalent equations. For example, you can get the equation $2x = 3$ from the equation $2x + 5 = 8$ by subtracting 5 from both sides.

Equivalent inequalities are similar to equivalent equations. Two inequalities are also called **equivalent** if they have the same solutions.

The concept is more complicated for inequalities, since an inequality usually has infinitely many solutions, while an equation often has only one solution. So keep in mind that, for two inequalities to be equivalent, *every solution* of each must also be a solution of the other.

Your task in this activity is to investigate whether the standard techniques for getting equivalent *equations* can also be used to produce equivalent *inequalities*.

You can start by working with the inequality $4x \leq 20$, and finding some numbers that satisfy this inequality.

Then try doing each of the following operations to the inequality $4x \leq 20$ to produce new inequalities:

• Add the same number to both sides of the inequality.

• Subtract the same number from both sides of the inequality.

• Multiply both sides of the inequality by the same non-zero number.

• Divide both sides of the inequality by the same non-zero number.

For each operation, do at least one example where "the same number" is *positive* and at least one where "the same number" is *negative*.

For each new inequality you create, decide whether the numbers that satisfy the new inequality are the same as those that satisfy the original inequality. In other words, investigate whether doing each of the operations to the inequality $4x \leq 20$ will produce an equivalent inequality.

Also think about what would happen if you started with a different inequality.

When you have completed your investigation, summarize your conclusions about working with inequalities.

▲ ▲ ▲ ▲ ▲ ▲ ▲ ▲

5. Discussion of *Investigating Inequalities*

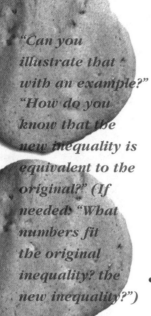

"Can you illustrate that with an example?" "How do you know that the new inequality is equivalent to the original?" (If needed: "What numbers fit the original inequality? the new inequality?")

When you think groups are ready, pull the class together for a whole-class discussion. Have students articulate why the various operations do or do not produce equivalent inequalities.

Insist that students use examples as part of their explanations. For example, to illustrate dividing an inequality by a constant, they might start from the condition $4x \leq 20$, divide by 4 to get $x \leq 5$, and then show that various numbers that satisfy the original inequality also satisfy the equivalent, and vice versa.

Note: For some students, the fact that inequalities with variables have infinitely many solutions may be an obstacle to understanding the effect of a particular operation. You may want to suggest that they look instead at inequality statements without variables. They can start with a true statement such as $5 \leq 12$ and see whether it stays true if something is done to both sides.

• *Multiplying (or dividing) by negative numbers*

The crucial case, of course, is that of multiplying (or dividing) an inequality by a negative number, since that is where the rules for inequalities differ from the rules for equations and where the confusion usually sets in.

If students go through their lists methodically, the issue of multiplying by a negative number will come up on its own. As an alternative, it may come up if students make a general statement like, "You can multiply both sides of an inequality by the same thing, and the result is equivalent."

In one way or another, they should confront the question of whether multiplying both sides of an inequality by a negative number gives an equivalent inequality. (The case of dividing is similar, and won't be discussed separately here.)

If necessary, you can ask someone to use the example $4x \leq 20$ to illustrate the idea of multiplying both sides by a negative number. If further prompting is needed, you can have students multiply each side of the inequality by a negative number, such as -3.

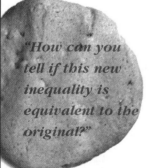

"How can you tell if this new inequality is equivalent to the original?"

Students should see that this gives the inequality $-12x \leq -60$. Ask students whether this is equivalent to the original. Their reaction should be to pick a number that satisfies the original inequality and to test it in the second.

Let's say they choose $x = 2$. (Be sure they pick something other than $x = 5$, which makes the two sides equal.)

They should see that $x = 2$ does not satisfy the new inequality since $-12 \cdot 2 > -60$.

This may require a review of what the ≤ symbol means when it is used with negative numbers. Thus, students need to know that –24 > –60, and not vice versa. You should probably go over this issue even if students seem able to use the symbol properly. Using the number line is probably the clearest way to make sense of the general definition of inequality.

• *Models for multiplication by –1*

If students seem confused about the reversal of sign, there are several approaches that you might use to help them understand.

Since the ideas below focus on multiplying by –1, you may want to point out that multiplying an equation by a negative number other than –1 can be broken into two steps.

For example, illustrate that, to multiply the inequality $4x ≤ 20$ by –3 (as above), you can multiply first by 3 and then by –1. The first step gives $12x ≤ 60$, which has no "direction" complications. Students should see that the problematic issue is understanding why you reverse the direction of an inequality when you multiply it by –1.

Number line reflection model: One approach to understanding multiplication of inequalities by –1 is based on the number line. Give students a numerical inequality such as 5 < 8 and ask them to explain this statement using the number line. They should be able to see that this just means that 5 is to the left of 8, as seen below.

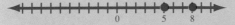

Then have students multiply each side of the inequality by –1, and have them describe what happens on the number line. They might use a phrase like "on the other side of 0" to describe where –5 and –8 are found.

Bring out the symmetry around 0, and focus on the idea that, since 8 is farther to the right than 5, its reflection around 0 ends up farther to the left. The discussion might produce a diagram like this:

An algebraic explanation based on addition: You can also use an algebraic approach based on addition to explain the effect of multiplying by –1. For example, start with the following inequality:

$$a < b$$

First have students add –b to both sides. Depending on your class, you may want to have students write this step explicitly as

$$a + (-b) < b + (-b)$$

and then simplify. Or they may go straight to the simplified statement:

$$a - b < 0$$

Similarly, they should then add –a to both sides, which gives

$$-b < -a$$

(perhaps with an intermediate step, as above).

Point out that this is the same as saying

$$-a > -b$$

so that the effect of the two addition steps is the same as the effect of multiplying both sides by –1 and reversing the direction of the inequality.

• *The ultimate rationale*

Ultimately, the reason for reversing inequalities when we multiply (or divide) by a negative number is that "it works." That is, a number that fits the original inequality (as $x = 2$ fits the inequality $4x \leq 20$ above) will generally not fit the inequality that we get by just multiplying both sides by the negative number, but it does fit if we reverse the direction of the inequality.

• *Summary: Comparing equations to inequalities*

Point out that reversing inequalities when multiplying both sides by a negative number is a major difference between equations and inequalities. With equations, we don't have to worry about the "direction" of the equality.

After this discussion, be sure to leave students assured that multiplying both sides of an inequality by a *positive* number will give an equivalent inequality.

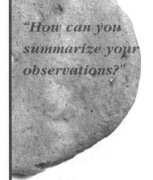

"How can you summarize your observations?"

Have students summarize the conclusions that they have reached. They should see that doing any of the following to an inequality will result in an equivalent inequality:

- Add the same number to both sides of the inequality.

- Subtract the same number from both sides of the inequality.

- Multiply both sides of the inequality by the same positive number.

- Divide both sides of the inequality by the same positive number.

- Multiply both sides of the inequality by the same negative number and reverse the direction of the inequality.

- Divide both sides of the inequality by the same negative number and reverse the direction of the inequality.

Teacher Maureen Burkhart of John Marshall High School in Los Angeles, CA, confers with a group.

6. Simplifying the *Baker's Choice* Inequalities

Throughout the unit, encourage students to simplify inequalities, using principles of equivalent inequalities. You can follow up the previous discussion by applying the ideas to the inequalities they have from the unit problem.

> *Note*: You may need to point out to students that the inequalities from the unit problem have two variables, while their previous work involved inequalities with at most one variable. Ask the class if they think the rules still apply. They should be able to see that, ultimately, the variables just represent numbers, so the same rules work.

For example, the preparation time constraint was expressed yesterday by the following inequality:

$$0.1x + 0.15y \leq 15$$

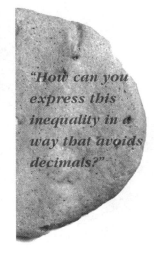

"How can you express this inequality in a way that avoids decimals?"

Ask students if they can express this condition in a way that avoids decimals. We would like them to see that the inequality above is equivalent to

$$10x + 15y \leq 1500$$

which they can get by multiplying both sides by 100. (Students may need some review work on decimals here, or they may end up with something like $x + 15y \leq 1500$.)

Students should be able to see that their new inequality is also equivalent to $2x + 3y \leq 300$. There is no "best" equivalent for the inequality, and there is no need to have students look for the greatest common divisor of the coefficients. It is often helpful, though, to eliminate decimals, so encourage students to simplify equations or inequalities when it is easy to do so.

Students should see simplification of inequalities as a matter of convenience rather than a matter of "right versus wrong." Students who prefer to leave the inequality $0.1x + 0.15y \leq 15$ in this form should be allowed to do so.

7. *Homework 3:*
Variables of
Your Own

If time allows, brainstorm different contexts in which students could use variables, other than those suggested in the assignment.

Student book page 7 →

Homework 3 Variables of Your Own

1. Make up a set of between 5 and 10 variables for a situation, similar to the list in *Homework 2: High School Letters*.

   For instance, you might call your situation Marching Band, Letters, Baseball Game Letters, Party Letters, or Clothing Store Letters. If you prefer, you can make up a situation of your own.

2. On the front side of your homework paper, write three expressions using your variables for which someone can write a summary phrase. On the back side, write the summary phrase.

3. On the front side of your homework paper, write three summary phrases for which someone can write an algebraic expression using your variables. On the back side, write the expression.

In the next class, you will exchange papers with other students and see if you can figure out the summary phrases and algebraic expressions for each other's situations.

DAY 4 *Picturing Cookies*

Ittoday's activity, students use graphs as a way to think about the constraints. It is very important that you let students proceed at their own pace on this.

Mathematical Topics

• Developing meaningful algebraic expressions
• Interpreting algebraic expressions in words using summary phrases
• Discovering how to graph linear inequalities
• Discovering the relationship between the graph of a linear inequality and the graph of the related linear equation

Outline of the Day

In Class

1. Discuss *Homework 3: Variables of Your Own*
2. *Picturing Cookies—Part I*
   • Students plot points that fit a given constraint inequality
   • Students develop the idea of the relationship between the graph of the inequality and the graph of the related equation

• Use "Issues to watch for students . . ." as needed
• Activity will be discussed on Day 5

At Home

3. *Homework 4: Inequality Stories*

1. Discussion of *Homework 3: Variables of Your Own*

You can either have groups exchange their homework or have students trade within their groups. In either case, have students try to find summary phrases for each other's expressions and expressions for each other's summary phrases. Meanwhile, circulate to see who did homework and to see how well your students understand this aspect of using variables.

2. *Picturing Cookies—Part I*

In today's activity, *Picturing Cookies—Part I,* students will work from scratch to develop the graph of one or more of the inequalities from the main unit problem. Experience indicates that even students who seem comfortable graphing linear equations are often not clear about the ideas in this activity, even if they have graphed inequalities before.

• *Introducing the activity*

To introduce the activity, you can refer the class to the list of constraint inequalities they compiled previously for the unit problem. Ask students how they think they could picture these constraints geometrically. If no one suggests graphing, ask them if that seems possible. Ask them how they would organize such a graph.

Help them to understand that, as with graphing an equation, graphing an inequality means marking all the number pairs that fit the condition. Students may not yet realize that the graph of an inequality is a two-dimensional area rather than a line or a curve, and you should let them discover this through the activity.

• *Doing the activity*

Let students work in groups on the activity *Picturing Cookies—Part I.* Give each group two sheets of grid chart paper to go with Questions 1–4 of this activity. (One sheet of grid chart paper is for students to experiment on initially and the other is to use after they have a sense of what their scales should be. Groups that move on to Question 5 will need more grid chart paper.)

By using the suggestions in the activity, students should be able to figure out how to graph one of these linear inequalities. (In *Picturing Cookies—Part II,* introduced on Day 7, they will look at combining graphs of inequalities.)

Use the notes in "Issues to watch for . . ." as a guideline for how to nudge students along if they are having difficulty. These are suggestions for you to keep in mind as you observe the students working in groups.

Be careful not to help the students too much. It is important that they eventually feel very comfortable with the graphing ideas in this activity. Ultimately, their understanding will be greater if they develop the ideas on their own.

Students may have trouble reading the instructions, but encourage them to keep struggling. They will be able to work through it, and they will be learning some important working skills as they do.

A whole-class discussion of the activity is scheduled for tomorrow. Students only need to deal with the first inequality. Question 5 is for groups that finish ahead of the rest.

"How should you label your axes?"

What color should (5, 10) be?

"What color should (40, 100) be?"

▼ ▼

While Students Are Working

Issues to watch for in Picturing Cookies—Part I

Be sure students realize that all members of a group should be using the same set of coordinate axes. As a group member finishes checking a number pair, that person adds the point, in the appropriate color, to the graph. The idea is to accumulate a lot of points quickly, so that students can see the overall idea.

You may want to remind students to label their axes appropriately (for example, as *number of dozens of plain cookies* and *number of dozens of iced cookies*).

It is not the intent of this activity that students simply graph the equation that goes with a constraint (for example, $x + 0.7y = 110$ for $x + 0.7y \leq 110$) and then shade one side. Although some students may have learned or seen this technique before, a major purpose of this activity is for students to *discover* the relationship between the graph of the equation and that of the inequality, or, if they have seen this idea before, to get a real sense of what this relationship is about and why it makes sense.

If you see students using the graph of the equation as the basis for their work, urge them to follow the specific directions of the activity. They should simply make up some pairs of numbers for x and y, test them in the inequality, and then color them appropriately.

If they are still stuck, you can ask them what color should be used for the number pair $x = 5$, $y = 10$. Since this pair satisfies the inequality $x + 0.7y \leq 110$, they should see that they should mark the point (5, 10) with the first color. Then have them make up more examples of their own.

Check that they include examples that don't fit the inequality, as well as those that do. For instance, if they try the pair $x = 100$, $y = 100$, they should see that it fails to satisfy the inequality, so they should mark the point (100, 100) with the second color.

As you circulate among groups, you may want to ask them about an example like (40, 100) in order to bring out that, if a number pair fits the equation $x + 0.7y = 110$, then it also fits the inequality $x + 0.7y \leq 110$.

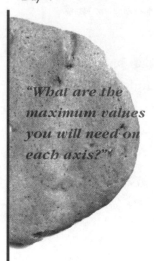

"What are the maximum values you will need on each axis?"

Selecting scales

After some experimentation, students may find that they can't fit points that don't work within their existing coordinate system. If you see them working with inappropriate scales, you can suggest that they redraw their work with new scales, and ask them to think about what scales might be appropriate.

They may see that, for this inequality, the largest values they will need for points that satisfy the inequality will be 110 for x and 157 for y. They should choose their scales so that they can show points that do not satisfy the inequality as well as points that do.

You may want to bring up this issue tomorrow as part of the class discussion, by asking if any groups had to adjust their scales after starting on the problem.

The "big picture"

Encourage students to keep plotting more and more points, both those that satisfy and those that do not satisfy the inequality. Presumably, they will eventually have an "aha!" and realize that the boundary between *satisfying the inequality* and *not satisfying the inequality* is the line corresponding to the equation $x + 0.7y = 110$. This is the "big picture" that is meant in Question 3.

Note: This unit assumes that students will recognize that the graph of the equation $x + 0.7y = 110$ is a straight line and will know how to draw this graph. Use your own judgment as to how much review of this is needed.

Question 5

If students get to the other constraints (Question 5), be aware that the "icing inequality" may present special problems since it involves only one variable. You can find suggestions for working with students on this at the end of tomorrow's notes for discussion of this activity. (See the subheading "The other constraints.")

• *The whole graph of the inequality*

The question of restricting x and y (that is, not allowing negative or fractional values) may well come up at some point in the context of this activity, either as students work in groups or in tomorrow's whole-class discussion. But keep in mind that the goal of this activity is for students to get insight into graphs of inequalities.

Therefore, if students are focusing on the graphs of the inequalities themselves (without reference to the appropriateness of the values), we recommend that you defer this issue until Day 7. The sections "First Quadrant Only" and "Whole Numbers Only?" on Day 7 give suggestions how to introduce and deal with these restrictions in the context of relevant problems.

There are two scenarios under which you may need to discuss the restriction issue. One is the case where students raise it on their own. The other is the case where students limit themselves to positive values, without seeing it as an issue, and, therefore do not get the complete graphs.

In either case, you can use the notes on Day 7 as well as comments on Day 2 (see "Restrictions on x and y") for guidance.

Emphasize that the focus of this activity is the graphing, and not how well the inequalities describe the problem. Therefore, at least for now, students should consider all numbers "eligible," and should only consider whether or not they fit the given condition.

Students need to plot enough points so that the "big picture" becomes clear.

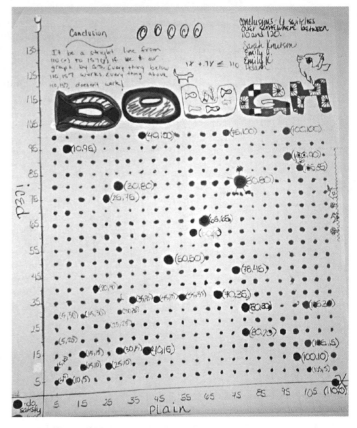

Picturing Cookies
—Part I

Student book page 8 →

By graphing relationships, we can turn symbolic relationships into geometric ones.

Since geometric relationships are visual, they are often easier to think about than algebraic statements.

One of the constraints in *Baker's Choice* is that the Woos can use at most 110 pounds of cookie dough. You can represent this constraint symbolically by the inequality $x + 0.7y \leq 110$, where x is the number of dozens of plain cookies and y is the number of dozens of iced cookies.

Choose one color to use for combinations of plain and iced cookies that satisfy the constraint. In other words, this color is for combinations that use 110 pounds or less of cookie dough. Choose a different color for combinations that do not satisfy the constraint, that is, for combinations that use more than 110 pounds of cookie dough.

For instance, 20 dozen plain cookies and 50 dozen iced cookies is a combination that satisfies the constraint, since this combination uses $20 + 0.7 \cdot 50$ pounds of cookie dough, for a total of only 55 pounds. That is, "$20 + 0.7 \cdot 50 \leq 110$" is a true statement. So the first color should be used for the point (20, 50).

But 100 dozen of each type of cookie does not satisfy the constraint, since this combination uses $100 + 0.7 \cdot 100$ pounds of cookie dough, for a total of 170 pounds. That is, the statement "$100 + 0.7 \cdot 100 \leq 110$" is not true. So the second color should be used for the point (100, 100).

Your task is to create a diagram showing both types of points, and then describe the graph of the inequality itself. (The graph of the inequality consists of all points that fit the constraint, that is, points of the first color.)

Steps 1–4 give details about what you need to do. Do your final diagram on a sheet of grid chart paper. If you have time, do Question 5, dealing with other constraints.

1. Each person in the group should try many pairs of numbers for the variables, testing whether or not each pair satisfies the constraint. *On one shared set of coordinate axes,* group members should each mark their number pairs using the appropriate color.

2. Make sure that your group has points of both colors. After some experimentation, you may need to change the scale on your axes so that you can show both types of points. If necessary, redraw your diagram with a new scale and replot the points that you have already found.

3. Continue with Parts 1 and 2, adding points of each type in the appropriate color. Keep plotting points until you get the "big picture," that is, until you are sure what the overall diagram looks like.

4. Include with your final diagram a statement explaining what you think the graph of the inequality itself looks like and why.

5. Repeat the process used in Parts 1–4 or use the "big picture" to graph the remaining constraints, each on its own set of axes.

▲ ▲ ▲ ▲ ▲ ▲ ▲

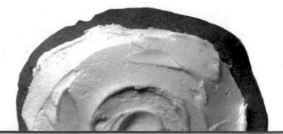

I think that our work on Baker's Choice *was really different from my previous experiences with math. We worked on a real life problem which could actually happen in my life instead of just working with numbers. We got a chance to put a lot of mathematics to use also. We got to do many parts of math at one time.*

**Rashaad, Student
Homework 14: Reflections on Learning**

3. *Homework 4:
Inequality Stories*

This assignment will give students more experience relating inequalities to real-world situations.

Homework 4   Inequality Stories

You have seen that certain real-world situations can be described using inequalities.

In the *Baker's Choice* problem, for example, each dozen plain cookies uses one pound of cookie dough and each dozen iced cookies uses 0.7 pounds of cookie dough, but the Woos have only 110 pounds of cookie dough.

Student book page 9 →

This limitation can be described by the "cookie dough inequality" $x + 0.7y \leq 110$, where x is the number of dozens of plain cookies and y is the number of dozens of iced cookies.

In this assignment, you will look more at the relationship between real-world situations and inequalities.

Part I: Stories to Inequalities

Use variables to write an inequality or set of inequalities that describes each of the following situations. Be sure to explain what your variables represent.

1. Margaret needs to build an enclosure for her new puppy, Callie. This will allow Callie to stay outside, but will keep her from running off and getting hurt. Margaret wants to build a rectangular enclosure and she has been told that Callie needs at least 60 square feet of space to play in.

   Margaret has to decide what dimensions to make the enclosure.

2. Lisa and Joel are a young couple furnishing a new house. They want to buy a computer, which will cost at least $1,500. (The exact cost depends on which special features they get.) Each is willing to contribute some money toward this purchase from their separate savings accounts.

   Joel's parents said they will contribute two dollars for every dollar that Joel contributes. Lisa's grandmother will exactly match Lisa's contribution.

   Joel and Lisa have to decide how much each of them will contribute to the computer purchase.

Part II: Inequalities to Stories

For each of the following inequalities, make up a real-world situation that the inequality describes. Again, be sure to explain what your variables represent.

3. $5x + 2y + 3z \leq 30$

4. $x^2 + y^2 > 81$

A student at West High School in Tracy, CA, explains her group's graph for Picturing Cookies—Part 1.

DAY 5

Continuing to Picture Cookies

> *Students summarize their work, seeing that the graph of each linear inequality is a half plane.*

Mathematical Topics

- Expressing situations with inequalities and illustrating inequalities with situations
- Seeing that the graph of a linear inequality is a half plane

Outline of the Day

In Class

1. Select presenters for tomorrow's discussion of *POW 1: The Broken Eggs*
2. Discuss *Homework 4: Inequality Stories*
   - Focus on clear definitions of variables
   - Expect varied responses
3. Discuss *Picturing Cookies—Part I* (activity from Day 4)
   - Focus on the relationship between an inequality and the related equation
   - Introduce the term **half plane**

4. *Optional:* Students share their own ideas and shortcuts for finding graphs of linear equations

At Home

5. *Homework 5: Group Reflection*

1. POW Presentation Preparation

Choose three students to make POW presentations tomorrow, and give them overhead pens and transparencies to take home to prepare. Since these will be the first students making POW presentations, you may prefer to use volunteers this time, rather than choosing students at random.

2. Discussion of *Homework 4: Inequality Stories*

You can assign one problem to each group to discuss in detail while you check off the homework (so there probably will be two groups working on each problem). You might suggest that each group working on Questions 3 and 4 select a couple of possible "stories."

Have the *club card* members of different groups report to the whole class on the group's discussion.

Be sure that the variables are clearly defined. Question 1 should be straight-forward, with an inequality like $LW \geq 60$ coming out of the presentation.

On Question 2, students should come up with something equivalent to $J + 2J + L + L \geq 1500$. (Some students may have trouble with the phrase "contribute two dollars for every one that Joel spends," and get $J + 0.5J + L + L \geq 1500$ by mistake.)

For Questions 3 and 4, students will probably have a wide variety of responses. For example, stories for Question 4 might involve distances, the Pythagorean Theorem, or area.

3. Discussion of *Picturing Cookies —Part I*

Different groups will probably grasp the idea of this activity at different rates. As soon as all groups are done with Questions 1–4 for the cookie dough constraint, you can have groups post their final diagrams and then bring the class together to discuss their work. After this discussion, you can have groups that finished other constraints present their results.

Caution: A group presenting its work may focus on its finished product, having understood clearly the relationship between the equation and the inequality. Other groups may still be unclear. Therefore, it is important to encourage the class to question the presenters until the explanation is clear to them.

In particular, make sure that the relationship between the inequality and the corresponding equation is clearly articulated. All students should see that the points on one side of the line are one color and that the points on the other side are the other color. Be sure to have students making presentations relate the different colors to the idea of *satisfying the inequality* and *not satisfying the inequality.*

"What is an easy way of describing where all the red (or blue) points are located?"

• *Why a half plane?*

Ask if someone can explain why all the solutions to the inequality are on one side of the line. In terms of the inequality $x + 0.7y \leq 110$, a student

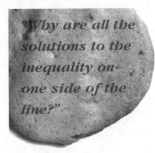

"Why are all the solutions to the inequality on one side of the line?"

might explain that, if you move to the left or down from the line $x + 0.7y = 110$, either x or y will decrease, so the value of $x + 0.7y$ will go down. If this value was equal to 110 *on the line,* then this value will be *less than* 110 to the lower left of the line.

Introduce the term **half plane** to describe the set of points that fit the inequality. This may need some explanation, since the term *plane* may be unfamiliar to some students.

In particular, be sure that students realize that a plane is infinite in extent. They might describe a plane as "an infinite flat surface." You need not get technical about the geometry here. You might point out that a half plane has somewhat the same relationship to a plane that a ray does to a line.

> You may find it necessary to remind students, in the context of this discussion, that a *line* is also infinite in extent.
>
> *Note*: The term *half plane* is sometimes defined to exclude the line itself. Be sure students realize that the graph of the inequality $x + 0.7y \leq 110$ includes the points on the line $x + 0.7y = 110$.

• *The other constraints*

Let students who worked with other constraints make presentations about the graphs. You may decide that you don't need to talk about all of them. However, you should probably take some time to consider the constraint $0.4y \leq 32$ (or an equivalent such as $4y \leq 320$ or $y \leq 80$), since the absence of the variable x may present a special difficulty. As a hint, you can ask students how they graph an *equality* with only one variable, such as $0.4y = 32$. Try to draw out the idea that x can be anything.

You may want to suggest rewriting this inequality as $0x + 0.4y \leq 32$. You can also refer back to the context of the problem, asking, "If the only restriction on the Woos was the amount of icing they had, how many dozens of plain and of iced cookies could be made?" Students should see that this constraint by itself does not limit the number of dozens of plain cookies at all.

4. *Optional:* Student Ideas on Graphing Linear Equations

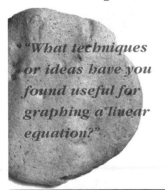

"What techniques or ideas have you found useful for graphing a linear equation?"

Now that students have a reasonably good grasp of the relationship between the graph of a linear inequality and the graph of the related equation, you may want to take some time to have students discuss ways they have found for graphing a linear equation. *Note:* Although students probably have studied this before, they may still feel uncomfortable. This is an opportunity to let them solidify their ideas on their own terms.

Let students brainstorm ways to do this. They may begin with the general idea that they can plot the graph by finding some points that satisfy the equation, and then connecting those points with a straight line.

Some students may realize that two points will suffice. Others may be aware that it's often good to plot three points, as a check in case one of them is incorrect. Moreover, some may notice that often the easiest points to find are the two intercepts, obtained by setting x equal to 0 and solving for y, and by setting y equal to 0 and solving for x.

It is not necessary that students learn any of these shortcuts, as long as they know at least *one* method for plotting the graph. But they will be graphing lots of linear equations during the unit (and probably in other settings as well), so it's only fair to give them a chance to share clever ways to do this.

5. Homework 5: Group Reflection

This assignment gives students a chance to reflect on their experience so far working in a group for much of their class time.

We recommend that you create new groups tomorrow.

Student book page 10 →

Homework 5 — Group Reflection

People play many roles when they work in groups. Of course, this is not only true in math classes.

This assignment is an opportunity for you to reflect on the way you participate in groups. Be as thoughtful as possible when you answer these questions because they are designed to help you.

Note: You don't have to share this homework with anyone other than your teacher, unless you want to.

1. a. Try to remember a time when you were in a group and you or someone else was left out of a discussion. Describe the situation. Did anyone try to include that person? If not, why not? If so, then how?

   b. What might you have done to help with the situation?

2. a. What has been your experience when someone has made a mistake in your group?

   b. How do you think groups should handle mistakes by group members?

3. a. Try to remember a time when you thought of saying something, or you did not understand something, but were afraid to speak out. Describe the situation, what you wanted to say, and why you did not say it.

   b. How do you wish you had handled the situation?

4. Discuss how the amount of homework preparation you do for class affects your participation in group discussions.

DAY
6

POW 1
Presentations

After POW presentations, students work on a new problem involving linear inequalities.

Mathematical Topics

• Looking at different ways to solve a word problem
• Expressing a situation in terms of variables and inequalities

Outline of the Day

In Class

1. Form new groups
2. Discuss *Homework 5: Group Reflection*
3. Presentations of *POW 1: The Broken Eggs*
   • Discuss expectations for listeners
   • Bring out the fact that there is more than one answer
   • Re-examine the POW write-up categories
4. *Healthy Animals*
   • Students express a new

situation in terms of variables and linear inequalities
   • Activity will be discussed on Day 7

At Home

5. *Homework 6: Graphing Healthy Animals*
6. *POW 2: Kick It!*
   • Clarify that only whole numbers should be used
   • POW is due on Day 11

1. Forming New Groups

This is a good time to form new random groups. However, you should balance the positive element of giving them a new set of group members with the drawback that they may have to start anew getting to know each other and learning to work together.

If you do create new groups, you can follow the procedure described on Day 1, recording the groups and the suit for each student.

2. Discussion of *Homework 5: Group Reflection*

Students need not share the homework assignment with one another unless they wish to do so, but you should collect the assignment so you can get a sense of how students feel about the group-work experience.

You might want to ask students whether they thought of any ways to encourage other students to feel more comfortable participating in groups.

Suggestion: If you want to get an overall sense of how students are responding to the unit, you might ask for feedback in connection with the homework discussion. Be aware, however, that *Homework 14: Reflections on Learning* will provide you with feedback near the end of the unit.

3. Presentations of *POW 1: The Broken Eggs*

Let the three students who were assigned yesterday make their presentations. Before beginning the presentations, you may want to discuss the expectations for listeners during presentations.

• *About listener behavior*

"Give me an example of how you can challenge someone politely."

You can start a discussion by asking students how they think listeners should behave during presentations.

Encourage students to ask questions during the presentations. You can emphasize that just listening politely—not challenging the speaker when one does not understand or does not agree—is not being a good listener. But you might also discuss how to be polite and respectful while challenging a speaker.

Remember that making a presentation can be very difficult for some students, and these first POW presenters might have a tough time. They deserve special consideration for volunteering.

• *After the presentations*

After the presentations are over, ask if other students have anything to add. Be sure students realize they can simply present an alternative method for getting an answer or explain an answer differently—they do not have to have a new or different answer.

If the presentations did not deal with the issue of the POW having more than one answer, bring that up now. Many students may have stopped when they found that 301 fits the given conditions, and may not have looked beyond that.

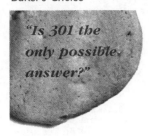

"Is 301 the only possible answer?"

You can simply ask if there are any other answers to the problem. Make students aware that this problem, like many others, has more than one answer, and that, in general, their goal should be to find as many answers as possible.

Important: The goal here is not for students to find the general expression for all possible solutions, but simply for them to recognize the issue of multiple solutions. If students want to work further on this problem, you can have them look at the supplemental problem, *More Broken Eggs.* (See Appendix.)

• *Another look at the POW write-up*

Finally, go over the parts of the POW write-up again and ask students to think back about what they could have included in each part. They will begin work on a new POW tonight, and you should expect their write-ups to improve on the next POW.

• *Your expectations for students*

Many of your students may not be used to writing in math class, to working on investigations, or to making presentations of their work. It may take some time for them to get used to what these things entail.

Your expectations for their work on this first POW should take their previous experience (or lack of it) into account. It is helpful to view this initial POW as an introduction to new ways of working, and focus on how students grow from this POW to the next.

4. *Healthy Animals*

Tell students that, in today's activity, *Healthy Animals,* and in tonight's homework, they will apply some things they have learned from working on the unit problem to a new situation. Unlike the cookie problem, this new problem has no expression to be maximized or minimized. Students work further on this situation in *Feasible Diets* on Day 8. *Note:* You may want to acknowledge to students that they are not done with the unit problem and tell them that they will get back to it tomorrow.

Students will each need a copy of the group's results for use in tonight's homework. If groups finish this activity, you can suggest that they begin work on the homework or on the new POW.

While Students Are Working

▼ ▼

It is important to allow students to make their own decisions about what variables to use, which axes to put them on, or what scales to use. In tomorrow's discussion of this activity, you can come to a class agreement on these issues.

Student book page 11 →

Healthy Animals

Curtis is concerned about the diet he is feeding his pet. A nutritionist has recommended that the pet's diet include at least 30 grams of protein and 16 grams of fat per day.

Curtis has two types of foods available—Food A and Food B.

Each ounce of Food A supplies 2 grams of protein and 4 grams of fat, while each ounce of Food B supplies 6 grams of protein and 2 grams of fat. Curtis's pet should not eat a total of more than 12 ounces of food per day.

Curtis would like to vary the diet for his pet within these requirements, and needs to know what the choices are.

1. Choose variables to represent the amount of each type of food Curtis will include in the daily diet. State clearly what the variables represent.

2. Use your variables to write inequalities to describe the constraints of the situation.

Adapted from a problem on p. 292 of Lial and Miller, *Mathematics With Applications*, Scott, Foresman and Company, Glenview, Illinois, 1987.

▲ ▲ ▲ ▲ ▲ ▲ ▲

5. *Homework 6: Graphing Healthy Animals*

This assignment continues the work from today's class activity.

Homework 6   Graphing Healthy Animals

Student book page 11 →

Define the variables you used in *Healthy Animals* and state the constraints you found for that problem.

Then make a graph of each of your constraints. Graph each constraint on a separate set of axes. For each graph, be sure to label your axes and show their scales.

*Tina Layne, Michelle Fasenmyer, and Kamran Malik,
students at Colton High School in Colton, CA,
present their work on* **Healthy Animals.**

6. *POW 2: Kick It!*

*"What's a field
goal?
a touchdown?"*

This problem gives students a chance to explore ways of combining numbers. They should come up with some conclusions about common divisors. You may want to point out that only whole-number scores are to be considered.

You may want to assure students that they do not need to know anything about football or its usual scoring system in order to be successful on this problem. They only need to know that, in this problem, there are two ways to score points, called *field goals* and *touchdowns.*

If you think that some additional information will make students more comfortable, you can add that field goals involve kicking the ball, while touchdowns involving running with it or throwing it. Be careful not to overwhelm students who are unfamiliar with football with more information than they need. For example, you don't need to get into the fact that, in standard football, there are other ways to score points.

This POW is scheduled for discussion on Day 11.

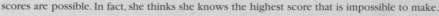

POW 2

Kick It!

The Free Thinkers Football League just has to be different. They aren't about to score their football games the way everyone else does. So they have thought up the following system:

Student book page 12 →

- Each field goal counts for 5 points.
- Each touchdown counts for 3 points.

The only way to score points in their league is with field goals or touchdowns or some combination of them.

One of the Free Thinkers has noticed that not every score is possible in their league. A score of 1 point isn't possible, and neither is 2 or 4. She thinks that, beyond a certain number, all scores are possible. In fact, she thinks she knows the highest score that is impossible to make.

1. Figure out what that highest impossible score is for the Free Thinkers Football League. Then write why you are sure that all higher scores are possible.

2. Make up some other scoring systems (using whole numbers) and see whether there are scores that are impossible to make. Is there always a highest impossible score? If you think so, explain why. If you think there aren't always highest impossible scores, find a rule for when there are and when there are not.

3. In the situations where there is a highest impossible score, see if you can find any patterns or rules to use to figure out what the highest impossible score is. You may find patterns that apply in some special cases.

Write-up

1. *Problem statement:* State the problem clearly in your own words. Your problem statement should be clear enough so that someone unfamiliar with the problem can understand what you are being asked to do.

2. *Process:* Based on your notes, describe what you did in attempting to solve this problem. Include a description of any scoring systems you examined in addition to the one given in the problem.

3. *Conclusions:*

   a. State what you decided is the highest impossible score for the Free Thinkers' scoring system. Explain both why you think that score is impossible and why you think all higher scores are possible.

   b. Describe any results you got for other systems. Include any general ideas or patterns you found that apply to all scoring systems, and explain why they apply in general.

4. *Evaluation:* Discuss your personal reaction to this problem. For example, comment on the following:

   - Was this problem too hard or too easy?
   - Did you enjoy working on it?
   - Did you consider it educationally worthwhile?
   - How would you change the problem to make it better?

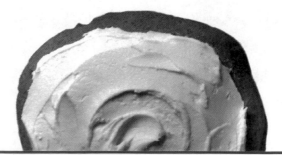

DAY 7 *Picturing Cookies Part II*

Today students begin putting the constraints together into a single graph.

Mathematical Topics

- Graphing inequalities
- Determining which side of a line is the graph of an inequality
- Restricting variables to the first quadrant or to whole numbers
- Combining graphs of linear inequalities

Outline of the Day

In Class

1. Discuss *Healthy Animals* and *Homework 6: Graphing Healthy Animals*
   - Define variables and develop the inequalities
   - Discuss the issue, "Which side of the line?"
2. First quadrant only (if not discussed previously)
   - Introduce new constraints to restrict the variables to non-negative values
3. *Picturing Cookies—Part II*
   - Students create a composite graph for inequalities from the unit problem

- Activity will be discussed on Day 8
4. Discuss whether to restrict variables to whole number values (if not discussed previously)
   - For now, have students ignore this restriction
   - Emphasize that this will have to be dealt with later if solutions are not whole numbers

At Home

5. *Homework 7: What's My Inequality?*

1. Discussion of *Healthy Animals* and Homework 6: *Graphing Healthy Animals*

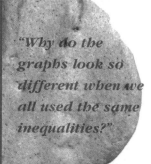

"Let's all use the same variables. What variables shall we use? What do they represent?"

As a class, decide on variables and what they represent. (It helps to have uniformity within the class on this. We use *a* and *b* for the number of ounces of Foods A and B, respectively.)

Let *diamond card* students from different groups give inequalities that they developed for the problem. They will probably come up with the following inequalities (or equivalents):

$$2a + 6b \geq 30 \qquad \text{(to guarantee enough protein)}$$

$$4a + 2b \geq 16 \qquad \text{(to guarantee enough fat)}$$

$$a + b \leq 12 \qquad \text{(to limit total intake)}$$

• *Graphs of the inequalities*

Once these inequalities are agreed on, let *diamond card* students from other groups present the graphs of these inequalities.

Other students may have very different-looking, but correct, graphs because of differences in how they labeled and scaled the axes.

"Why do the graphs look so different when we all used the same inequalities?"

Using *a* and *b* as the variables, it's natural to follow alphabetical order and use *a* for the horizontal axis and *b* for the vertical axis. But some students may have used different variables—or simply not have followed alphabetical order—and so they may have correct graphs that appear different from those presented.

Differences in scale may also result in a different appearance to graphs, so be alert to these variations and the confusion they may cause for students.

> *Note:* Since this problem will be revisited tomorrow in the activity *Feasible Diets,* you may want to establish agreement now on labels and scales for the axes and urge students to save their work. But be sure to acknowledge to students that there is no "right" labeling or scaling for the graphs from the homework.

• *Which side of the line?*

Notice that, for the first two of the inequalities listed above, the graph is the area above and to the right of the graph of the related equation. By contrast, all the graphs of the inequalities in the unit problem, *Baker's Choice,* are below and to the left of the related equation. So this is a good time to ask students how to tell which side of the line you want.

"How do you tell which side of the line you want?"

Perhaps the simplest method is to pick a point that is off the line, and see if it satisfies the inequality or not. For example, to see if the inequality $2a + 6b \geq 30$ represents the half plane above the line $2a + 6b = 30$ or the half plane below that line, consider an easy point such as $(0, 0)$. This point is *below* the line, and does *not* satisfy the inequality $2a + 6b \geq 30$. Therefore the points that *do* satisfy the inequality form the half plane *above* the line.

Similarly, the point $(2, 0)$ is below the line $a + b = 12$, and satisfies the inequality $a + b \leq 12$. Therefore, the graph of the inequality $a + b \leq 12$ must be the half plane *below* the line $a + b = 12$.

Note: It may seem obvious that "$\geq$" means *above* and "$\leq$" means *below*. But the inequality $a + b \leq 12$ is the same as $12 \geq a + b$, so the direction of the inequality sign doesn't by itself determine which side of the line represents the graph of the inequality.

Also, it is not obvious what to do when there are variables on both sides of the inequality, as in the inequality $2x \geq y - 3$.

The question of which side of a line to use is confusing to many students. Having them try to learn a system of rules (for instance, involving signs of coefficients) may lead to unnecessary anxiety about graphing inequalities. Instead, we recommend that they just test an example or two to decide which side of the line they want in a given situation. This is a system which will help them become confident about their own skills.

2. First Quadrant Only

If it hasn't yet been discussed, this is a good time to bring up the fact that it often doesn't make sense in a real-life problem for variables to be negative. In *Healthy Animals,* both a and b must be non-negative.

It may be especially helpful to discuss this issue on this problem, since you can do it without raising the other restriction issue mentioned on Day 2, namely, limiting the values of the variables to integers. In *Healthy Animals,* all non-negative numbers make sense.

Here is one way to bring up this idea:

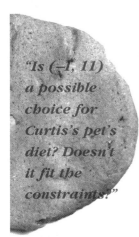

"Is (–1, 11) a possible choice for Curtis's pet's diet? Doesn't it fit the constraints?"

While looking at the graph from one of the inequalities, for instance $2a + 6b \geq 30$, ask whether a specific point, for example, $(-1, 11)$, is a possible choice for Curtis's pet's diet. If students say no, argue that the coordinates do satisfy the inequality, and in fact satisfy all three inequalities, and therefore the point should be an option for Curtis.

Presumably, students will say that this doesn't make sense, that is, an amount of food cannot be negative. Emphasize that this condition does not come from any of the three constraint inequalities presented above, but is inherent in the meaning of the variables in the problem context.

"How can you eliminate negative values but still get the complete graphs of the individual inequalities?"

You can suggest to students that they need to distinguish between the problem of finding possible diets for Curtis's pet and the problem of graphing the particular inequality. If they are doing the latter, then the point (-1, 11) should be included, since it satisfies the inequality. But, of course, they don't want to allow "-1 ounces of Food A, 11 ounces of Food B" as an acceptable diet for Curtis's pet.

Then ask how they could impose the non-negativity condition on the overall problem and not put restrictions on the graphs of the individual inequalities. As a hint, you can suggest that they put additional inequalities into the problem. They should see that they can do this by adding two additional constraints, namely, $a \geq 0$ and $b \geq 0$.

In anticipation of the next activity, you may want to suggest that students make a similar adjustment to their constraint list for the original *Baker's Choice* problem (posted on Day 2). Or you may prefer to see if they make this adjustment on their own as they work on the activity.

3. *Picturing Cookies —Part II*

In *Picturing Cookies—Part I,* students learned how to graph each of the inequalities from the unit problem, *Baker's Choice.*

Today, in *Picturing Cookies—Part II,* they look at how to combine the graphs of the inequalities. They will discuss this activity tomorrow.

Suggestion: If some groups finish early, you can ask them to work on the POW within their groups. If no time is available today, you may want to provide some other class time for students to get started on the POW.

The major new idea for this activity is the principle that the set of points that simultaneously satisfy more than one linear inequality is the intersection or overlap of the individual half planes for the separate inequalities.

This is analogous to the use of the term *intersection* in the context of graphs of equations. There, as here, it refers to the set of points that lie on the graphs for two or more different conditions. The intersection points represent solutions that are common to the different conditions.

In the case of linear equations and their graphs, *intersection* simply refers to the point where the lines cross. This special case is important later in this unit. This activity takes students step-by-step through the analogous process, both for the sake of review and because the case of inequalities is more complex and more intimidating than that of equalities.

▼▼▼▼▼▼▼▼▼▼▼▼▼▼▼▼▼▼▼▼▼▼▼▼▼▼▼▼

While students are working, you can check that they are following the directions correctly (shading only the points that fit the inequality, changing colors for each new inequality, and so on).

You may also need to remind them to make a separate graph as described in Question 4.

If the issue of whole-number values for x and y hasn't come up before, it should definitely come up in connection with this activity. You can raise it with individual groups as they work. (See below.) If you wish, you can wait until tomorrow's whole-class discussion to see if students bring it up on their own.

4. Whole Numbers Only?

As mentioned on Day 2, the values for x and y in the answer to the Woos' problem should probably be whole numbers (or at least multiples of $\frac{1}{12}$).

"Does (52.35, 28.71) fit the constraints? Could these be the numbers of dozens of each kind of cookie?"

If you need to bring this issue up yourself, you can simply identify some point that fits all the constraints, such as (52.35, 28.71), and ask if the Woos could make that many dozens of plain and iced cookies. Students will probably agree that this doesn't make sense.

No matter how the issue comes up, you can point out that, in graphs like these, with values of 100 and more for x and y, it would be very awkward to try to graph individually each point having whole-number coordinates. Suggest that, as a start, they work with the complete graphs of the inequalities, including points whose coordinates are not whole numbers. These graphs can still provide us with a useful picture, even though they contain extraneous points.

Tell students that, for now, they should just graph the inequalities themselves, and they can worry later about how fully the inequalities model the real-world situation. If it turns out that the point that gives the maximum profit has coordinates that are "ineligible," they will have to decide where to go from there.

In this problem, the maximum profit does occur at a point with whole number coordinates. In problems where this is not the case, the task of finding the optimal whole number solution can be quite complicated. (Taking the whole number point closest to the optimal overall solution does not always give the optimal whole number solution.)

Jacquay Pickens and Sugey Ochoa, students at Colton High School in Colton, CA, graph the constraints for Healthy Animals.

Student book page 13 →

Picturing Cookies —Part II

You have already worked with each of the constraints from the *Baker's Choice* problem on its own set of axes. Each graph gives you a picture of what that constraint means.

Now you need to see how to combine these constraints to get one picture of all of them together.

1. Begin with one of the constraints that you worked on before. Using a colored pencil, color the set of points that satisfy this constraint. *Note:* Unlike your work on *Picturing Pictures—Part I,* you should *not* color the points that do not satisfy the constraint.

2. Now choose a second constraint from the problem.

   a. On the *same set of axes,* but using a *different color,* color the set of points that satisfy this new constraint.

   b. Using your work so far, identify those points which satisfy *both* your new constraint and the constraint you used in Question 1.

3. Continue with the other constraints, using the same set of axes. Use a new color for each new constraint.

   a. Color the points that satisfy each new constraint.

   b. After graphing each new constraint, identify the points that satisfy all the constraints you have graphed so far.

4. When you have finished all the constraints, look at your overall work. Make a single new graph which shows the set of all points that represent possible combinations of the two types of cookies that the Woos can make.

   In your graph, show all the lines that come from the constraints, labeled with their equations.

5. *Homework 7: What's My Inequality?*

In this homework, students reverse the process of the work they've been doing, now going from graph to inequality.

Student book page 14 →

Homework 7   What's My Inequality

Graphs of inequalities can play an important role in understanding problem situations. So far in this unit, you have started with the inequality and found its graph. In this assignment, you go in the opposite direction.

For each graph below, find an inequality that represents the shaded area. (You should imagine that the shaded area continues indefinitely, including all points on the shaded side of the given line.)

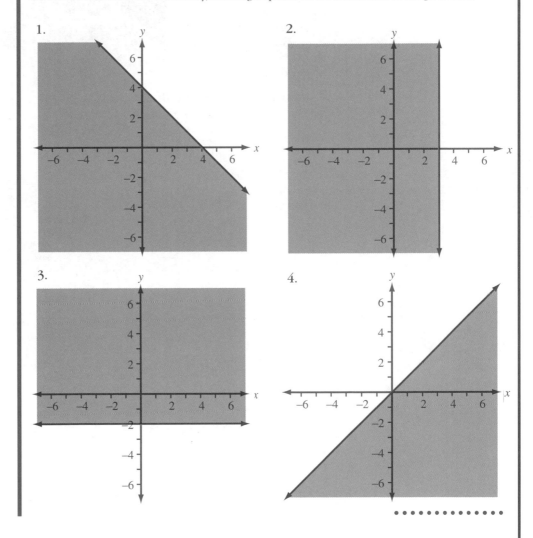

Angel Torres makes a presentation to the class. A transparency his group prepared in advance clarifies ideas and holds his classmates' attention.

DAY 8 *The Cookie Region*

Mathematical Topics

- Finding inequalities to describe half planes
- Combining the graphs of linear inequalities
- Introducing the term **feasible region**
- Finding feasible regions

Outline of the Day

In Class

1. Discuss *Homework 7: What's My Inequality?*
   - Strict versus non-strict inequalities
2. Discuss *Picturing Cookies— Part II* (from Day 7)
   - Introduce the terms **feasible point** and **feasible region**
3. *Feasible Diets*
   - Students apply the concept of feasible region to the situation from *Healthy Animals* (from Day 6)
   - No whole-class discussion is needed

At Home

4. *Homework 8: Picturing Pictures*

1. Discussion of *Homework 7: What's My Inequality?*

You can ask different groups to prepare presentations on how they found the inequality for one of the graphs in the homework, choosing groups that finished work yesterday on *Picturing Cookies—Part II*. Meanwhile, other groups can finish work on *Picturing Cookies—Part II*.

You probably won't want more than one presentation on each homework problem, and you may not need to do all four problems.

Have the *heart card* students give the homework presentations, discussing how they decided on the inequalities. Students may begin on some problems by finding the equation of the line itself.

Question 1 should be easy once students have this equation. On Questions 2 and 3, some students may be confused by the fact that the equation for the line involves only one variable. You may want to review the graph of the inequality $0.4y \leq 32$ from the unit problem.

Question 4 may present some difficulty, since none of the equations corresponding to inequalities in the *Baker's Choice* problem had a positive slope. The hard part will most likely be deciding whether this region is the graph of $x \leq y$ or of $y \leq x$. Probably the best way for students to do this is just to test some points in the shaded region.

• *Strict versus non-strict inequalities*

The assignment is somewhat ambiguous about whether students should use **strict inequalities** for their answers on this homework. (A *strict inequality* uses < or >, rather than ≤ or ≥.) For example, there is no way for students to decide from the graph of Question 1 whether it represents $x + y \leq 4$ or $x + y < 4$.

You can tell students that some books show a dotted line for the boundary of a region when the boundary itself is not part of the graph. By this convention, one would use a dotted line for the boundary of the graph of an inequality such as $x + y < 4$, and the graph as shown in Question 1 of the homework would represent the inequality $x + y \leq 4$.

2. Discussion of *Picturing Cookies —Part II*

"Where did that inequality come from?"

"What does that line represent?"

"Why do we want the points on this side of the line rather than on the other side?"

Ask for one or two volunteers to present their combined graphs from *Picturing Cookies—Part II*. Insist that they explain how they got their region, going through the inequalities one at a time.

During the presentations, you can ask the rest of the class questions like the following to check that they understand:

• Where did that inequality come from?

• What does that line represent?

• Why do we want the points on this side of the line rather than on the other side?

• Are points on the line part of the region?

"Are points on the line part of the region?"

"What does the final graph tell you about the cookie problem?"

Be sure that the entire process gets tied together at the end. That is, make sure that students don't get so involved in the details of individual inequalities that they forget the connection of the graphs to the original *Baker's Choice* problem.

They should be able to articulate that the points that have been colored every time represent the Woos' choices. Be sure that the "First Quadrant Only" issue has been dealt with (see Day 7), by including the constraints $x \geq 0$ and $y \geq 0$.

• *Feasible region and feasible points*

You should play up the importance of the final graph (Question 4), perhaps asking students what they would call this region. Tell them that, in standard mathematics terminology, this set is called the **feasible region** for the set of inequalities and individual points in the region are called **feasible points**. This is the first of several feasible regions that students will draw.

You may want to comment on the everyday use of the word *feasible* to mean "possible" or "capable of being done."

Note: You need not worry about whether or not students get the coordinates of the points of intersection at this time. If they found them, fine, but if not, that can wait until later in the unit. Students will return to the unit problem, *Baker's Choice,* on Day 14, when they might make a fairly fresh start. The general issue of finding points of intersection will be discussed on Day 10.

For your convenience: The shaded area in this graph shows the feasible region for the cookie problem.

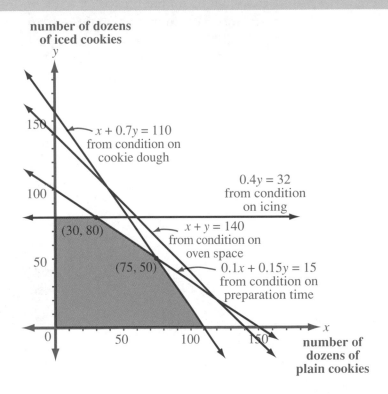

number of dozens of iced cookies

$x + 0.7y = 110$
from condition on cookie dough

$0.4y = 32$
from condition on icing

$x + y = 140$
from condition on oven space

$0.1x + 0.15y = 15$
from condition on preparation time

(30, 80)

(75, 50)

number of dozens of plain cookies

"What does it mean that the oven space line misses the feasible region?"

• *An extraneous constraint*

Notice that the line $x + y = 140$, which comes from the limitation on the amount of oven space available, misses the region completely.

You can ask students what this fact means. One way of expressing its significance is that, because of the other constraints, it wouldn't help the Woos to have an unlimited supply of oven space. Another way of saying this is that, because the Woos must satisfy all the other constraints, they can't make use of all of their available oven space.

• *Two fine points*

You may want to take the opportunity now to bring out two other ideas:

- We are dealing with *linear* inequalities and their corre-

sponding *linear* equations here. This fact makes it easy to describe the area defined by each inequality because it is just a half plane.

- We often get lazy about distinguishing between an equation and its graph. For example, we sometimes say "the line $x + y = 140$" when we really mean "the line which is the graph of the equation $x + y = 140$." The interconnectedness of the ideas of equation and graph can never be overemphasized.

You can probably find other places as well in the unit to bring out these ideas.

3. *Feasible Diets*

To follow up on the preceding work with the concept of feasible region, let students work in groups on the activity *Feasible Diets,* in which they draw the feasible region for the pet-diet problem, *Healthy Animals* (from Day 6). *Reminder:* They graphed the individual inequalities in *Homework 6: Graphing Healthy Animals,* but did not put them together as they are asked to do here.

Use your judgment about whether or not this needs to be discussed as a whole class. No specific discussion notes are provided.

*For your convenience:
The feasible region for
this problem is the
shaded area
in the graph.*

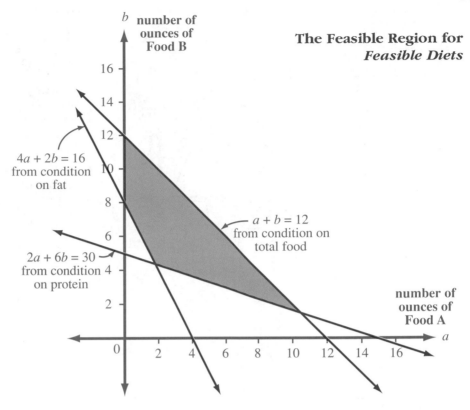

The Feasible Region for
Feasible Diets

b number of
ounces of
Food B

$4a + 2b = 16$
from condition
on fat

$a + b = 12$
from condition on
total food

$2a + 6b = 30$
from condition
on protein

number of
ounces of
Food A

a

▼ ▼

**While Students
Are Working**

In drawing the feasible region, students will need to take into
account that the variables must be non-negative, probably using
the inequalities $a \geq 0$ and $b \geq 0$ introduced on Day 7. Without these
constraints, the feasible region above would continue across the
vertical axis to the intersection in the second quadrant of the two
lines $4a + 2b = 16$ and $a + b = 12$.

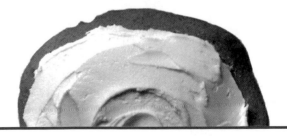

*"Should (−1, 11)
be in the feasible
region? Is it a
possible solution
to the problem?"*

If you see them making this mistake, you can identify a point that
fits the three original inequalities, such as (−1, 11), and ask
whether this should be in the feasible region. If needed, follow up
by asking if this is a possible solution to the problem.

Reminder: There is no function to be maximized or minimized in
this problem.

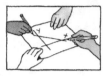

or

Student book page 15 →

Feasible Diets

In *Homework 6: Graphing Healthy Animals,* you graphed the individual constraints from the problem *Healthy Animals.*

Now, your task is to draw the feasible region for that problem.

Here are the key facts from *Healthy Animals:*

- Curtis's pet needs at least 30 grams of protein.
- Curtis's pet needs at least 16 grams of fat.
- Each ounce of Food A supplies 2 grams of protein and 4 grams of fat.
- Each ounce of Food B supplies 6 grams of protein and 2 grams of fat.
- Curtis's pet should not eat a total of more than 12 ounces of food per day.

Be sure to identify your variables, label your axes, and show the scales on the axes.

▲▲▲▲▲▲▲▲

4. Homework 8: Picturing Pictures

Tonight's homework introduces a new problem and reinforces the graphing work done earlier. It returns to the issue of maximizing profit, which has not been considered since Day 2.

Student book page 16 →

Homework 8 Picturing Pictures

Hassan is an artist who specializes in geometric designs. He is trying to get ready for a street fair next month.

Hassan paints both watercolors and pastels. Each type of picture takes him about the same amount of time to paint. He figures he has time to make a total of at most 16 pictures.

The materials for each pastel will cost him $5 and the materials for each watercolor will cost him $15. He has $180 to spend on materials.

Hassan makes a profit of $40 on each pastel and a profit of $100 on each watercolor.

1. Use symbols to represent Hassan's constraints.

2. Make a graph that shows Hassan's feasible region; that is, the graph should show all the combinations of watercolors and pastels that satisfy his constraints.

3. For at least five points on your graph, find the profit that Hassan would make for that combination.

DAY 9

Profitable Pictures

Mathematical Topics

- Seeing that setting a linear expression equal to different contraints gives a family of parallel lines
- Maximizing a linear function on a polygonal region

Outline of the Day

In Class

1. Discuss *Homework 8: Picturing Pictures*
   - Post a graph of the feasible region for later use
   - Identify the profit function
2. *Profitable Pictures*
   - Students find combinations that yield a given profit
   - Activity will be discussed on Day 10

At Home

3. *Homework 9: Curtis and Hassan Make Choices*

1. Discussion of Homework 8: Picturing Pictures

As a class, decide on variables to be used in the discussion. We will use p for the number of pastels and w for the number of watercolors.

"How can you represent Hassan's time constraint symbolically? his cost constraint?"

Ask the class how to represent the two constraints symbolically, perhaps choosing students at random (for example, by picking cards). They should get inequalities equivalent to the following:

$$p + w \leq 16 \qquad \text{(for the number of pictures)}$$

$$5p + 15w \leq 180 \qquad \text{(for the money available for materials)}$$

"How can you organize this information?"

Students may remember to include the inequalities $p \geq 0$ and $w \geq 0$. If not, you can bring this up as they sketch the feasible region.

Have students offer points they used for Question 3, perhaps having a volunteer plot them as they are suggested. Tell students to mentally check that these suggested points satisfy all of the constraints.

As points are offered, you may want to have students make a chart with various points and the profit they found at each of those points. It can look like this:

Number of Pastels	Number of Watercolors	Profit on Pastels	Profit on Watercolors	Total Profit
5	3	$200	$300	$500

Continue until there are enough points to sketch the region, or until students say that you just need to draw the lines corresponding to the equations $p + w = 16$ and $5p + 15w = 180$, and shade in the intersection of the half planes to the lower left of the lines. If necessary, bring out the fact that only the first quadrant is relevant to the problem, because of the inequalities $w \geq 0$ and $p \geq 0$.

For your convenience: The feasible region for the *Picturing Pictures* problem should look like the shaded area of the following graph:

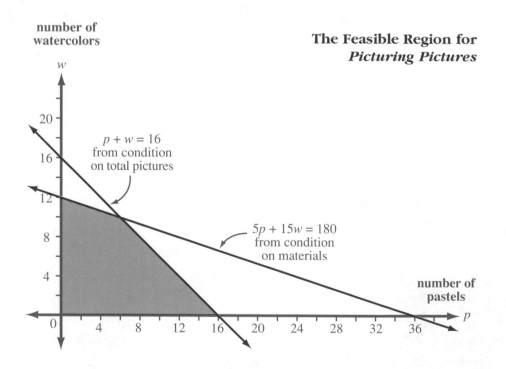

Post this graph for further use today and tomorrow.

"What does this graph tell you?"

Note: You will probably want a transparency of this region for tomorrow's discussion of the next activity. A large diagram for making this transparency is included at the end of today's section.

Ask students to articulate what this graph means. They should recognize that each point in the feasible region (or at least each whole number point) represents a possible choice Hassan can make about how many pictures of each type to make.

Comment: The issue of limiting the variables to whole numbers may come up again here, as it did for the cookie problem. That is, students may point out that they shouldn't be shading the entire region bounded by the lines, but only marking the points with whole number coordinates. If this point is raised, you can review the ideas from the earlier discussion of this issue—see the section "Whole Numbers Only?" on Day 7.

• *The profit function*

"What combination gives the greatest profit? Why?"

Also ask students to express the profit function in terms of their variables. In terms of our p and w, the profit function is $40p + 100w$.

You can pose the question of what combination gives the greatest profit. If someone thinks they know, let them present their answer and explanation. But don't expect students to get any definitive explanations at this stage of the discussion. They will know both the answer and a good explanation by the end of tomorrow.

Caution: Some students may have read the amounts $40 and $100 as selling prices rather than profits, since that was the way information was presented in the unit problem, *Baker's Choice.* It is important that students notice the difference before they begin work on today's activity, *Profitable Pictures.*

2. *Profitable Pictures*

Ask the students to work in their groups on the activity *Profitable Pictures.*

Students will continue their work on this activity tomorrow. During tomorrow's work, each group prepares a report on this activity, which should include answers to Questions 1–4, but should be focused especially on Question 5.

Suggestion: If groups have trouble finding combinations that yield a specific profit, you may want to suggest that they consider points outside the feasible region as well as points in the region.

Student book page 17 →

Profitable Pictures

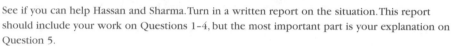

Hassan asked his friend Sharma for advice about what combination of pictures to make.

She thought he should figure out a fair profit for that month's work, and then paint what he needed to achieve that profit.

Here are the facts you need from *Homework 8: Picturing Pictures:*

- Each pastel requires $5 in materials and earns a profit of $40 for Hassan.

- Each watercolor requires $15 in materials and earns a profit of $100 for Hassan.

- Hassan has $180 to spend on materials.

- Hassan can make at most 16 pictures.

See if you can help Hassan and Sharma. Turn in a written report on the situation. This report should include your work on Questions 1–4, but the most important part is your explanation on Question 5.

1. You have already found the feasible region for the problem, which is the set of points that satisfy the constraints. On graph paper, make a copy of this feasible region to use in this problem. Label your axes and show the scales.

2. Suppose Hassan decided $1000 would be a fair amount to make.

    a. Find three different combinations of watercolors and pastels that would make Hassan a profit of exactly $1000.

    b. Mark these three number pairs on your graph from Part 1.

3. Now, suppose Hassan wants to make only $500. Find three different combinations of watercolors and pastels that make Hassan a profit of exactly $500. *Using a different-colored pencil,* add those points to your graph.

4. Next, suppose that Hassan wants to make $600. Find three different combinations of watercolors and pastels that make Hassan a profit of exactly $600. *Using a different-colored pencil,* add those points to your graph.

5. Well, Hassan's mother has appeared on the scene and she thinks that he should try to earn as much as possible.

    Now, Hassan wants to figure out the most he can make within his constraints. He also wants to be able to prove to his mother that it is really the most. Please help Hassan with this problem.

    a. Find out the maximum possible profit that Hassan can make and what combination of pictures he should make to earn that profit.

    b. Write an explanation that proves your answer is correct.

▲ ▲ ▲ ▲ ▲ ▲ ▲

3. *Homework 9: Curtis and Hassan Make Choices*

This is a fairly straightforward assignment, intended to strengthen students' understanding that profit (or cost) lines form a parallel family.

No specific discussion is scheduled for this assignment, but you may want to use students' work on these problems in connection with tomorrow's discussion of *Profitable Pictures.*

Homework 9   Curtis and Hassan Make Choices

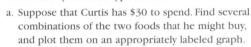

Student book page 18 →

1. Curtis goes into the pet store to buy a substantial supply of food for his pet. He sees that Food A costs $2 per pound and that Food B costs $3 per pound.

   Since he intends to vary his pet's diet from day to day anyway, he isn't especially concerned about how much he buys of each type of food.

   a. Suppose that Curtis has $30 to spend. Find several combinations of the two foods that he might buy, and plot them on an appropriately labeled graph.

   b. Now do the same thing assuming that Curtis spends $50, using the same set of axes.

   c. What do you notice about your answers to Questions 1a and 1b?

2. Hassan has a feeling that there's going to be a big demand for his work. He is considering changing his prices so that he makes a profit of $50 on each pastel and $175 on each watercolor.

   a. Based on these new profits for each type of picture, find some combinations of watercolors and pastels so that Hassan's total profit would be $700, and plot them on a graph.

      (The combinations you give here don't have to fit Hassan's usual constraints.)

   b. Now do the same for a total profit of $1750, using the same set of axes.

   c. What do you notice about your answers to Questions 2a and 2b?

If graphing calculators are readily available, students like Edith Hernandez will learn to use them spontaneously and flexibly.

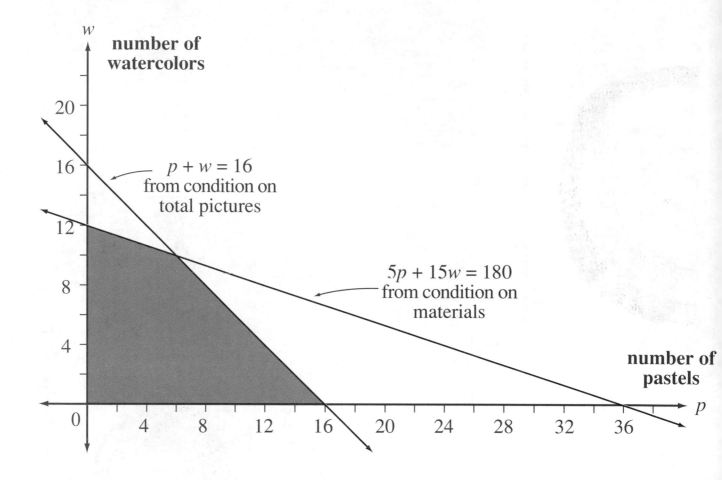

w

number of watercolors

20

16    $p + w = 16$
from condition on
total pictures

12

                        $5p + 15w = 180$
8   from condition on
                        materials

4   **number of
pastels**

0   4   8   12   16   20   24   28   32   36 p

Feasible Region for
Picturing Pictures

DAY 10

Continuing to Profit from Pictures

Students use a family of parallel profit lines to locate the combination that maximizes profit.

Mathematical Topics

- Seeing that setting a linear expression equal to different constants gives a family of parallel lines
- Maximizing a linear function on a polygonal region
- Seeing how changing a problem's parameters changes the solution
- Relating *point of intersection* to *common solution*

Special Materials Needed

- A transparency of the feasible region (Find it at the end of Day 9 notes.)

Outline of the Day

In Class

1. Select presenters for tomorrow's discussion of *POW 2: Kick It!*
2. Provide additional time as needed for students to continue their work on *Profitable Pictures* (from Day 9)
3. Discuss *Profitable Pictures*
   - Introduce the term **profit line**
   - Focus on the fact that different profits give parallel lines
   - Profit is maximized at the most extreme point where the family of profit lines intersects the feasible region
4. Discuss ways to find the point of intersection of the graphs of two linear equations

At Home

5. *Homework 10: You Are What You Eat*

   Note: This guide suggests that you omit having a separate discussion for *Homework 9: Curtis and Hassan Make Choices.* You might look at this homework briefly as part of the discussion of *Profitable Pictures* (in connection with parallel profit lines).

1. POW Presentation Preparation

Choose three students at random (perhaps using cards) to make POW presentations tomorrow, and give them overhead pens and transparencies to take home to prepare. Do not choose any students who presented *POW 1: The Broken Eggs.*

2. Continuation of *Profitable Pictures*

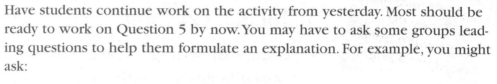

"What do you notice about combinations that produce a given profit?" "What happens as the profit increases?"

Have students continue work on the activity from yesterday. Most should be ready to work on Question 5 by now. You may have to ask some groups leading questions to help them formulate an explanation. For example, you might ask:

- What do you notice about combinations that produce a given profit?

- What happens as the profit increases?

At some point, you may want to remind students to prepare written reports for this activity.

When most groups seem to have gotten as far with Question 5 as they are going to get, begin the discussion.

Note: If you have groups that finish early, you can suggest that they work on the supplemental problem, *Hassan's a Hit!* (see Appendix), which builds on Question 2 of last night's homework.

3. Discussion of *Profitable Pictures*

You can start the discussion by putting the transparency of yesterday's graph on the overhead and having different students each mark a point from Question 2—a way for Hassan to make exactly $1000. The only whole number points that give this profit are (0, 10), (5, 8), and (10, 6).

(*Note:* See "The points for each profit are collinear" on the next page.)

Then have students from different groups give the points they used for Question 3, and mark them on the transparency. Be sure to use a different color for this, so the points are distinguishable. The only whole number points in the feasible region that give a profit of exactly $500 are (0, 5), (5, 3), and (10, 1).

Finally, look at Question 4. There are *four* whole number points in the feasible region that yield the given profit: (0, 6), (5, 4), (10, 2), and (15, 0).

• The points for each profit are collinear

Either as presenters do each problem or after all three sets of points are drawn (in different colors for each profit), ask students what they notice about the different groups of points. It is essential that they recognize that, for each profit, the points that give that profit lie on a straight line.

Introduce the term **profit line** for the set of points with a given profit, and have students draw the complete lines, connecting the individual points that students found in Questions 2–4. You can extend these profit lines to include points outside the feasible region. The line will also include points whose coordinates are not whole numbers, even though Hassan cannot make fractions of pictures.

You may also want to have students check points on each line, including some that are outside the feasible region, to see that they would give the right profit, even if Hassan can not use them. That is, have students estimate the coordinates of points on the line and see what profit each gives. These profits should be approximately the same as the profit for the points they plotted originally.

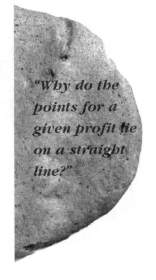

"Why do the points for a given profit lie on a straight line?"

Ask if students can explain why the points for a given profit lie on a straight line. If necessary, ask what condition the coordinates must satisfy for a point to give a profit of $1000. Yesterday students identified the profit function as $40p + 100w$. Now they should be able to see that, for a combination of paintings to give a profit of $1000, the coordinates must satisfy the equation $40p + 100w = 1000$. They should also recognize this as the equation of a straight line.

For your convenience: The diagram should now look something like this:

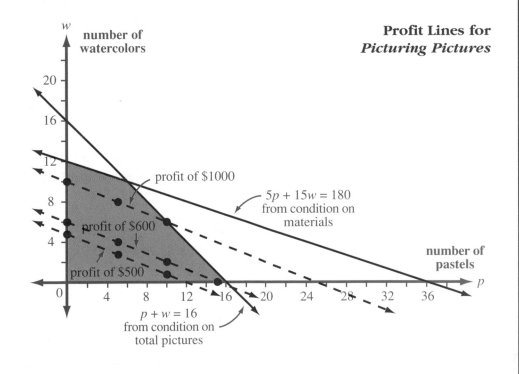

• *Profit lines are parallel*

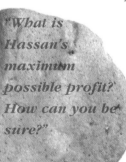

"What do you notice about the set of profit lines?"

A crucial element of this analysis is that all the profit lines are parallel. If it hasn't yet been mentioned, ask the class what they notice about these lines.

If it hasn't already been done, insist that students draw the actual lines, and label each with the profit amount that it represents. This should make it clearer that these are *parallel lines,* and that, as the profit increases, the line "slides" upward to the right.

You can use the algebraic representations of the different lines to reinforce the visual evidence that the lines are parallel. Thus, students should already have seen that the profit lines have the following equations:

- For a profit of $1000: $40p + 100w = 1000$

- For a profit of $500: $40p + 100w = 500$

- For a profit of $600: $40p + 100w = 600$

Students may reason in various ways to see that these lines are parallel.

One approach is to see, for example, that the equations $40p + 100w = 1,000$ and $40p + 100w = 500$ cannot have any solutions in common, since the expression $40p + 100w$ cannot be equal to both 1,000 and 500. Since the equations have no common solutions, the graphs have no common points. Since these lines have no points in common, they must be parallel.

Students may also use the similarity among the equations to formulate an explanation based on slope. In either case, the discussion should assure students that the lines are genuinely parallel, and don't just *seem* to be parallel on the graph.

Note: You may want to insert a brief discussion here of last night's *Homework 9: Curtis and Hassan Make Choices,* to confirm that students got parallel cost or profit lines on those problems. You can have students express each cost or profit line as an equation so that they see the similarity in the algebraic forms.

• *Maximizing profit*

"What is Hassan's maximum possible profit? How can you be sure?"

Now ask several groups to state what they think is the maximum overall profit Hassan can make and ask some groups to present a justification of their answer.

Roughly, the reasoning should begin with the following ideas:

- The points that give a specific profit satisfy an equation that has a form similar to those listed above:

$$40p + 100w = \text{profit}$$

- For any particular profit, these points will lie on a line which is parallel to the three lines they have from Questions 2–4.

• Within this family of parallel lines, profit goes up as the line chosen is farther up and to the right.

From here, students should see intuitively that they want to "slide" one of these parallel lines up and to the right until it is about to leave the feasible region. If the sketch is done carefully, they will see that, among those lines in the family that actually intersect the feasible region, the most "extreme" line is the one through the point where the two lines $p + w = 16$ and $5p + 15w = 180$ intersect. (See the following subsection "Which is the most extreme point?".)

Therefore, the point where these two lines intersect represents the maximum profit. Because this reasoning is so visual, most students should be able to understand it, even if they didn't discover it on their own.

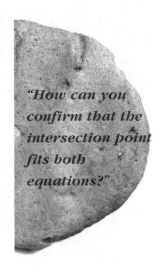

"How can you confirm that the intersection point fits both equations?"

Probably at least some students will have found the coordinates of this point, (6, 10), by trial and error or by other means. (If not, you can have them do so now, perhaps by estimating from the graph.) No matter how the coordinates are found, you will probably want to have students confirm that this point fits both equations.

You can have students find Hassan's profit for this combination of pictures, perhaps comparing it to any earlier values that they thought were optimal.

The section "Points of Intersection" later today presents some ideas to bring out about points of intersection as well as ways to handle the task of finding the point.

• *Which is the most extreme point?*

Since the profit lines are almost parallel to the line $5p + 15w = 180$, it may not be clear from the students' graphs where the family of parallel lines leaves the feasible region.

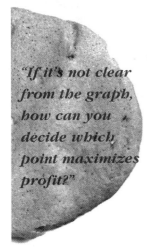

"If it's not clear from the graph, how can you decide which point maximizes profit?"

If this uncertainty is raised, you can ask students what other points seem likely. They should see from the graph that the point (0, 12) is also a reasonable candidate. Ask students how they can be sure which point is the right one if they don't trust their graphs.

They should see that they can just compute the profit at the two points and compare. They will see that the point (6, 10) (6 pastels and 10 watercolors) gives a profit of $1240 while the point (0, 12) (just 12 watercolors) gives a profit of only $1200.

Note: The next two homework assignments involve a new problem and variations on it, and give students an opportunity to study how a change in the parameters of a problem can affect the solution.

Day 10

Baker's Choice

• The case of profit lines parallel to a constraint line

Students may wonder what to do when the family of parallel lines is *parallel* to a boundary of the feasible region. In that case, all points on that boundary will give the same profit. You can have an interesting discussion about how to make a decision in that case.

For example, Hassan might decide which point to use along that boundary on the basis of what he likes to paint, since profit is the same. In the unit problem, *Baker's Choice*, if one boundary of the feasible region were parallel to the family of parallel lines, the Woos might decide to choose the point along that boundary that maximizes the number of plain cookies, because they think that plain cookies are healthier.

Optional: You may want to ask students to look for a pair of profits for each type of picture that would create profit lines parallel to a constraint line. Question 2 of *Homework 11: Changing What You Eat* provides an example of this.

• For teachers: What are the goals of this unit?

Students may soon realize that the feasible region is always a polygon and

that the place where the family of parallel lines leaves the region is always a vertex (or an entire side) of that polygon.

But it is *not* a goal of this unit that students learn that the maximum is always at a vertex. Rather, as stated in the *Overview,* the goal is for students to deepen their understanding of the relationship between equations or inequalities and their graphs and for them to reason and solve problems using graphs.

In particular, students should learn about parallel lines, should reason geometrically, and should use various ways, both algebraic and graphical, to find the common solution to a pair of linear equations.

Therefore, when they are solving a particular problem, they should be expected to go back to the "family of parallel lines" reasoning which explains *why* the maximum (or minimum) occurs at a vertex. Simply finding all the vertices and comparing profit (or whatever is being maximized or minimized) should not be considered as sufficient explanation for why a particular point gives the maximum.

4. Points of Intersection

Note: If there is no time for this today, you can do it tomorrow after the POW presentations.

Students saw in *Profitable Pictures* that the point they wanted was the point where the two lines $p + w = 16$ and $5p + 15w = 180$ intersect. To answer Hassan's question, they needed to find the coordinates of this point of intersection. They may have used different methods to do this, such as estimation or

Interactive Mathematics Program

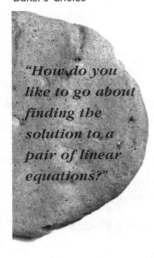

"How do you like to go about finding the solution to a pair of linear equations?"

algebra, but this is a good occasion for a general discussion of how to solve pairs of linear equations.

You may want to point out that the equations in *Profitable Pictures* are particularly simple and to mention that, in other situations, trial and error might not suffice, especially if the solution involves fractions.

There are several approaches that students may use. One approach is to use algebraic techniques to solve the pair of equations, but other methods will work as well. It is not the purpose of this unit to teach students algebraic techniques for finding solutions to pairs of linear equations.

You may want to return to your regular textbook to review this subject. As an alternative to that, a supplemental activity, *Get the Point?,* is included (see Appendix) which leads students to discover the substitution method for solving systems of linear equations. Another supplemental activity, *Charity Rock,* provides a context in which students set up and solve such a system.

In the case of Hassan and his pictures, the equations are simple enough that trial and error probably sufficed for students to find that $p = 6$ and $w = 10$ gives the point that the two lines have in common. You can encourage students to use trial and error as a reasonable first approach.

Another good approach to finding the coordinates is estimation from the graph. Since the coordinates are actually whole numbers in the Hassan problem, this method gives the exact value.

If students find the numbers by trial and error or by applying an algebraic technique, you can urge them to check that their answer looks like a good approximation to the coordinates of the point on the graph.

On the other hand, if they find the numbers by estimating the coordinates from the graph, they should check that the numbers do actually satisfy both equations.

Whatever method students use to find this point, you can bring out that the values they find for p and w have two distinct but closely related properties:

- These numbers are the p and w coordinates of the point where the two lines intersect.

- These numbers are the values for p and w that satisfy both of the equations.

In other words, use this opportunity to make sure that students understand the connection between the concepts of equation and graph.

5. *Homework 10: You Are What You Eat*

Students will probably approach this problem using the techniques of the past few days, although they can also use a more intuitive approach.

Student book page 19 →

Homework 10   You Are What You Eat

The Hernandez twins do not like breakfast. Given a choice, they would rather skip breakfast and concentrate on lunch.

When pressed, the only things they will eat for breakfast are Sugar Glops and Sweetums cereals. (The twins are allergic to milk, so they eat their cereal dry.)

Mr. Hernandez, on the other hand, has the strange idea that his children should eat breakfast every single morning. He also believes that their breakfast should be nutritious. Specifically, he would like each of them to get at least 5 grams of protein and not more than 50 grams of carbohydrate each morning.

The Sugar Glops package says that each ounce has 2 grams of protein and 15 grams of carbohydrate. The Sweetums box says that every ounce of Sweetums contains 1 gram of protein and 10 grams of carbohydrate.

So what is the least amount of cereal each twin can eat while satisfying their father's requirements? (Mr. Hernandez wants a proof that his criteria are met, and the twins want a proof that there is no way they can eat less.)

DAY 11 POW 2 Presentations

After POW presentations, students use a feasible region to answer the home-work problem, this time looking for a minimum.

Mathematical Topics

- Developing conjectures and proofs concerning linear combinations of positive integers
- Continue working with feasible regions
- Minimizing a linear expression subject to linear constraints

Outline of the Day

In Class
1. Form new groups
2. Presentations of *POW 2: Kick It!*
   - Work with students to develop explanations of their results
3. Discuss *Homework 10: You Are What You Eat*
   - Set up inequalities, find the feasible region, and identify the solution

At Home
4. *Homework 11: Changing What You Eat*

1. Forming New Groups

This is an excellent time to form new random groups. Follow the procedure described on Day 1, recording the groups and the suit for each student.

2. Presentations of *POW 2: Kick It!*

Ask the three students you selected yesterday to make their presentations. Presumably, in Question 1, they will have found that the highest impossible score is 7. The focus in this question should be on their reasoning as to why every higher score is possible, and the quality of their explanations may vary.

Possible hint: "Can you find a sequence of consecutive scores that are possible? How can you get larger scores from those in the sequence?"

If the presenters are having difficulty developing a convincing explanation, a general approach you can suggest is that they get a sequence of consecutive scores that are possible, and then see how every larger score can be obtained from a score in that sequence.

For example, students might show explicitly that all scores from 10 through 19 are possible, and then observe that they can get any larger score by adding 10 points (2 field goals) as often as necessary to one of these scores. For instance, they can get a score of 47 by taking the scoring combination that gives 17 and adding 6 additional field goals.

Comment: More "efficient" variations of this proof are possible, but using multiples of 10 makes this one comparatively easy for students to see.

• *Questions 2 and 3*

On chart paper, write down all the conclusions the presenters mentioned, either in connection with other specific scoring systems or as general principles. For each conclusion, ask someone to present a proof, an explanation that shows that the conclusion is true. If there are some conclusions for which no satisfactory proof is given, you can put them on a separate sheet of chart paper and label them **conjectures.**

Ask other students to volunteer conclusions and proofs that weren't mentioned by a presenter. Your goal is to get students to improve their explanations and to search for reasons.

• • • • • • • • • • • • • • • • • • • •

What I was asked to do was find the highest impossible number that you can not get by adding the numbers 5 and 3 however many ways you can. You can use the numbers as many times as you want.

Curtis, Student Write-Up for *POW 2: Kick It!*

• *Sample conclusions and proofs*

The following notes give some examples of conclusions and proofs that might arise. We urge you not to read these until you have worked on the problem yourself. We also caution that these ideas are intended as background information for you and not as a set of expectations of what students should do.

Example 1

The first example concerns a case where there is no highest impossible score.

> *Conclusion:* If the number of points for a field goal is 2 and the number of points for a touchdown is 8, then there is no highest impossible score.

Proof: You can only get even scores in this game, so every odd number is impossible. Since there is no highest odd number, there is no highest impossible score.

Comment: You may get several conclusions of this type. The familiar terminology of *even* and *odd* makes this example easier to state than a case where the scores are, for example, 5 and 15.

If you get several cases like this, you may want to try to move students toward the following more general statement of the conclusion:

> *Conclusion:* If the number of points for a field goal is more than 1 and divides the number of points for a touchdown, then there is no highest impossible score.

Proof: All the scores made only with field goals are multiples of the points for one field goal. Since the points for each touchdown are also multiples of that number, then all possible combinations of the two are multiples of that number. Then every number that is not a multiple is impossible. Since we can always find a number larger than any given one that isn't a multiple, there is no highest impossible score.

Note: This is stated in terms of the score for a field goal dividing the score for a touchdown, but it works just as well the other way around. See "Further background information for teachers" (below) for an even better generalization.

Example 2

The next example concerns a family of cases where there *is* a highest impossible score. The reasoning is similar to that for the specific case mentioned in the POW.

Conclusion: If the number of points for a field goal is 2 and the number of points for a touchdown is odd, then the highest impossible score is 2 less than the score for a touchdown.

Proof: You can get any even score from field goals, and you can get any odd score above the value of a touchdown by adding one touchdown and the right number of field goals. But you can't get any odd numbers less than the value of a touchdown.

• *Further background information for teachers*

The following observations also apply to this POW. This information is pre-sented simply as background information, and not as material that should be presented to the class. A POW investigation is intended to open doors for students, but it is not intended to present a topic that students need to master.

You may want to use some of these ideas as topics for students to pursue for extra credit or just for the fun of further exploration.

a. Whenever the two numbers have a common factor bigger than 1, all scores are multiples of that common factor, so there are arbitrarily high impossible scores. This is an even better generalization of Example 1 than that given earlier. (For example, it includes a case like 6 points for a field goal and 8 points for a touchdown.) Explaining this should be within students' grasp.

b. Conversely, if the two numbers are *relatively prime* (have no common factor except 1), then there is a highest impossible score. However, proving this in general is difficult, and probably beyond the reach of the students.

c. A general rule for finding the highest impossible score is $ab - (a + b)$, where a and b are the two point-values and a and b are relatively prime. Some students may find this formula through examples, but the proof is difficult. Students also may find formulas for special "families." For example, as indicated in Example 2, if a field goal is worth 2 points, and a touchdown is worth an odd number of points, then the highest impossible score is 2 less than the value of a touchdown.

3. Discussion of *Homework 10: You Are What You Eat*

"What combination of cereals with the least total amount will satisfy Mr. Hernandez?"

Ask each group to decide on the combination with the least amount of cereal that will satisfy Mr. Hernandez. Then choose one group to present its solution.

Students will probably set this up like their previous problems. If they use x for the number of ounces of Sugar Glops and y for the number of ounces of Sweetums, then the constraints are:

$$2x + y \geq 5 \qquad \text{(to guarantee enough protein)}$$
$$15x + 10y \leq 50 \qquad \text{(to avoid too much carbohydrate)}$$
$$x \geq 0, \, y \geq 0 \qquad \text{(since the amounts cannot be negative)}$$

They should also identify what quantity they are minimizing—the twins' goal is to minimize $x + y$.

For your convenience: The shaded area in the following graph shows the feasible region for this problem as well as a sample "consumption line" showing combinations for which the twins eat a total of one ounce of cereal.

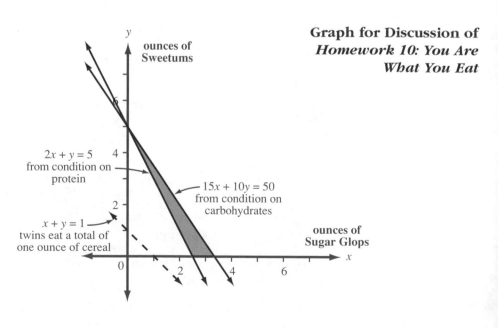

Graph for Discussion of *Homework 10: You Are What You Eat*

$2x + y = 5$
from condition on protein

$15x + 10y = 50$
from condition on carbohydrates

$x + y = 1$
twins eat a total of one ounce of cereal

ounces of Sweetums

ounces of Sugar Glops

The "lowest" consumption line that intersects the feasible region is the one through the point $(2\frac{1}{2}, 0)$, which is where the line $2x + y = 5$ intersects the x-axis. Therefore, $2\frac{1}{2}$ ounces of Sugar Glops (and no Sweetums) is the best solution from the twins' point of view.

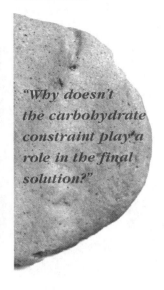

"Why doesn't the carbohydrate constraint play a role in the final solution?"

You can point out that the carbohydrate constraint does not play a role in the final solution to the problem, and ask students why this is the case. They should say something to the effect that the limit of 50 grams of carbohydrate is high enough that the twins get their requirement of protein without getting close to the carbohydrate limit. Since they want to eat as little as possible anyway, the carbohydrate condition is not a problem.

It may be worthwhile to have students look at how the graph reflects that the carbohydrate condition is immaterial. The pair of cereal quantities must be at or above the "protein line" in order for the twins to get enough protein. Since the point on this line that uses the least cereal is $(2\frac{1}{2}, 0)$, all that matters as far as carbohydrate is concerned is that this point be at or below the "carbohydrate line," which it is.

Note: Students may come up with explanations for this solution without making a graph. For example, they may point out that the twins get more protein per ounce from Sugar Glops than from Sweetums, so there is no reason to eat any Sweetums. If they present this reasoning, they need to check that $2\frac{1}{2}$ ounces of Sugar Glops does not provide too much carbohydrate.

4. *Homework 11: Changing What You Eat*

Tonight's homework asks students to examine the way the specific numbers affect the solution to the cereal problem. They should see that these numbers can even affect whether or not there is a solution.

If time is available, you may want to have students start this assignment during class.

Mark Hansen, Jennifer Rodriguez, Karla Viramontes, and Robin LeFevre, students at Colton High School in Colton, CA, make a group graph.

Homework 11   Changing What You Eat

Student book page 20 →

In *Homework 10: You Are What You Eat,* the twins' solution was to just eat Sugar Glops.

That way, they could get their protein by eating only $2\frac{1}{2}$ ounces of cereal and still not get too many grams of carbohydrate.

But what if the cereals had been a little different from the way they were in that problem, or if Mr. Hernandez had been stricter about the twins' carbohydrates, or ... ?

Here are some specific variations for you to think about.

1. Suppose that Sugar Glops is the same as in the original problem (with 2 grams of protein and 15 grams of carbohydrate per ounce), but that now Sweetums also has 2 grams of protein per ounce (and still has only 10 grams of carbohydrate per ounce).

   Also suppose that Mr. Hernandez still has a 50-gram limit on carbohydrate and still wants each of them to get at least 5 grams of protein.

   How much of each cereal should the twins eat if they want to eat as little cereal as possible?

2. Now suppose that Sugar Glops has 3 grams of protein and 20 grams of carbohydrate per ounce, and Sweetums is the same as in Problem 1 (2 grams of protein and 10 grams of carbohydrate per ounce).

   Also suppose that Mr. Hernandez has now decided that the twins can't eat more than 30 grams of carbohydrate (but they still need at least 5 grams of protein).

   What should the twins do?

3. Make up a variation on the problem where the twins would choose to eat just Sweetums.

4. Make up a variation on the problem where there would be no solution.

DAY 12 *Rock 'n' Rap*

Students look at a new problem about two kinds of CDs.

Mathematical Topics

- Continue working on how changing a problem's parameters changes the solution
- Continue working with the idea of a family of parallel lines in relation to a feasible region

Outline of the Day

In Class

1. Discuss *Homework 11: Changing What You Eat*
   - Focus on how changing parameters changes the solution
2. *Rock 'n' Rap*
   - Students apply the method of "family of parallel lines" to a new situation
3. Discuss *Rock 'n' Rap*
   - Use the problem to review that the point of intersection of two lines is the same as the common solution to the two equations

At Home

4. *Optional: Homework 12: Getting on Good Terms*

1. Discussion of *Homework 11: Changing What You Eat*

You may want to let students spend a few minutes in their groups comparing results and problems, and then have *spade card* students present the different problems. You will probably want more than one presentation for Questions 3 and 4.

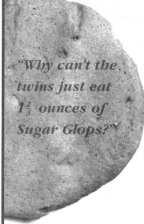

In Question 1, students should see that the twins should eat $2\frac{1}{2}$ ounces of cereal but that any $2\frac{1}{2}$-ounce combination will do. That is, any such combination represents the minimum amount of cereal that provides enough protein and not too much carbohydrate.

The diagram below shows the feasible region for this problem. In this case, one of the constraint lines, $2x + 2y = 5$, is parallel to the family of consumption lines, so any point along this line represents the minimum amount of cereal.

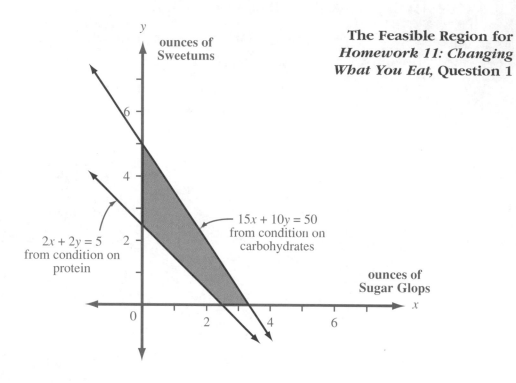

The Feasible Region for *Homework 11: Changing What You Eat*, Question 1

$2x + 2y = 5$
from condition on protein

$15x + 10y = 50$
from condition on carbohydrates

ounces of Sweetums

ounces of Sugar Glops

In Question 2, however, the twins can't eat only Sugar Glops, even though $1\frac{2}{3}$ ounces of Sugar Glops provides enough protein with the minimum amount of cereal, because $1\frac{2}{3}$ ounces of Sugar Glops has too much carbohydrate. Therefore, they need to include some Sweetums, which has less carbohydrate per ounce. It turns out that exactly one ounce of each cereal meets the requirements with the least total cereal, as you can see in the following diagram of the feasible region.

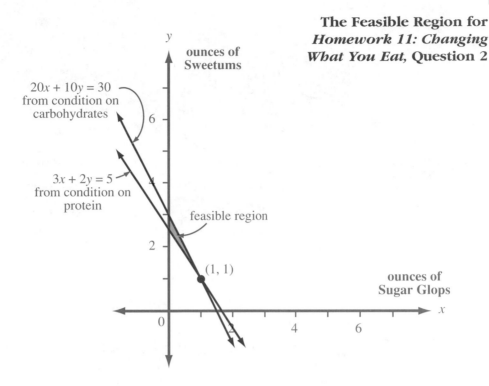

The Feasible Region for
Homework 11: Changing
What You Eat, **Question 2**

ounces of Sweetums

$20x + 10y = 30$
from condition on
carbohydrates

$3x + 2y = 5$
from condition on
protein

feasible region

$(1, 1)$

ounces of
Sugar Glops

After the discussion of Questions 1 and 2, you can let volunteers present variations they made up for Questions 3 and 4. Use your judgment about how much time to spend on this.

2. *Rock 'n' Rap*

The next activity, *Rock 'n' Rap,* provides a new problem on which students can put their new concepts and techniques to work. This problem is used tomorrow as a vehicle for exploring the use of the graphing calculator.

In this problem, the point of maximum profit will be at the intersection of the lines $y = x$ and $1,500x + 1,200y = 15,000$ (using x for the number of rock CDs and y for the number of rap CDs). Students should at least get to the stage of looking for the coordinates of that point. Their level of algebra skills will determine how they find those coordinates and how you handle this aspect of the problem.

In Question 3, with the different profit arrangement, students should see that the profit line has a different slope and that, with this amended diagram, the profit is a maximum at the point where the line $1,500x + 1,200y = 15,000$ intersects the x-axis.

Some students may be able to see intuitively that, on Question 1, the greatest profit will be made by making as many rap CDs as possible within the constraints. The only reason not to make only rap CDs is the distributor's restriction not to release more rap than rock. Rap CDs cost less to produce, and use more production time than rock CDs, and produce greater profit than rock CDs.

Note: The condition "they will not release more rap music than rock" is often confusing to students, perhaps because it is stated negatively. You may want to suggest that students look at numerical cases to clarify how to express this as an inequality.

**While Students
Are Working**

▼ ▼

Whether or not students see the solution intuitively, urge them to draw the feasible region, and then use the reasoning discussed in *Profitable Pictures*. As a hint, you can ask groups to list the steps of their reasoning in that problem. They should come up with a list something like this:

- We graphed the feasible region.

- We graphed possible combinations for a given profit, and got a straight line.

- We varied the particular profit, and got a family of parallel lines.

- We saw that, as the profit increased, the parallel line shifted up and to the right.

- We looked for the line in the family that was farthest "up and to the right" but still crossed the feasible region.

- The point where this line crossed the region was the point we wanted.

Students at Roosevelt High School in Los Angeles, CA, work together to graph constraints.

Student book page 21 →

Rock 'n' Rap

The *Hits on a Shoestring* music company is trying to plan its next month's work. The company makes CDs of both rock and rap groups.

It costs them an average of $1500 to produce a rock CD and an average of $1200 to produce a rap CD. (The higher cost for rock comes from needing more instrumentalists for rock CDs.) It takes about 18 hours to produce a rock CD, while a rap CD takes 25 hours.

The company can afford to spend up to $15,000 on production next month. Also, according to the company's agreement with the employee union, the company must spend at least 175 hours on production.

Hits on a Shoestring makes $20,000 in profit on each rock CD they produce and $30,000 in profit on each rap CD they produce.

The company recently promised their distributor that they will not release more rap music than rock, because the distributor thinks the company is more closely associated with rock in the public mind.

1. Find out how many CDs they should make of each type next month to maximize their profit. (They can make a fraction of a CD next month and finish it the month after.)

2. Explain your process of arriving at an answer to Question 1 and the reason why you think your answer gives a maximum profit.

3. Suppose the profit situation is reversed and the company made $30,000 profit on each rock CD and $20,000 profit on each rap CD. Would this change your advice to them about how many to make of each type to maximize their profit? Explain your answer.

▲ ▲ ▲ ▲ ▲ ▲ ▲

3. Discussion of Rock 'n' Rap

"What are the constraints in the problem?"

You can begin the discussion by asking several *club card* students to give constraints for this problem.

If x is used to represent the number of rock CDs and y is used to represent the number of rap CDs, the constraints are:

$1,500x + 1,200y \leq 15,000$ (for the amount of money available for production)

$18x + 25y \geq 175$ (for the amount of production time the company owes the union)

$y \leq x$ (as promised to the distributor)

$x \geq 0, y \geq 0$ (since the numbers can't be negative)

Suggestion: Ask students to simplify the first inequality. Either $15x + 12y \leq 150$ or $5x + 4y \leq 50$ is easier to work with than $1,500x + 1,200y \leq 15,000$.

Then you can have another *club card* student draw the feasible region on the overhead, showing how the inequalities already given lead to the desired region.

For your convenience: The shaded area in the following graph shows the feasible region for this problem.

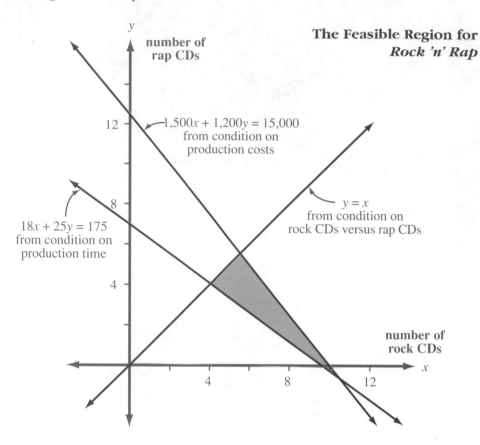

The Feasible Region for
Rock 'n' Rap

y

number of
rap CDs

12 — $1,500x + 1,200y = 15,000$
from condition on
production costs

8 — $y = x$
from condition on
rock CDs versus rap CDs

$18x + 25y = 175$
from condition on
production time

4

number of
rock CDs

x

4   8   12

• Maximizing profit

Once students have drawn the region and discussed it, have the class identify the function that expresses the profit in terms of x and y (namely, $20,000x + 30,000y$).

Then ask one or more students to explain how to find the point on the graph that maximizes profit. This has two aspects:

- Explaining why the desired point is at the intersection of the two lines $y = x$ and $1,500x + 1,200y = 15,000$

- Finding the coordinates of this point of intersection

Here are some ideas on how students might handle each part.

• Identifying the point

To explain the location of the desired point, students will probably use the "family of parallel lines" reasoning.

For example, using a profit of $120,000, they might graph the equation $20,000x + 30,000y = 120,000$. They may know enough about graphing linear equations by now to use the two intercepts, (6, 0) and (0, 4), as guides for drawing the graph.

"What expression represents profit?"
"What point maximizes profit?"

Note: You may want to have students choose at least two possible profits, and draw the lines that correspond to these profits. Although only one such line is needed to know what the "parallel family" is, encourage students to do another to review that all possible profits give parallel lines. These profit lines do not necessarily have to intersect the feasible region.

The following graph shows the feasible region and the profit line $20,000x + 30,000y = 120,000$.

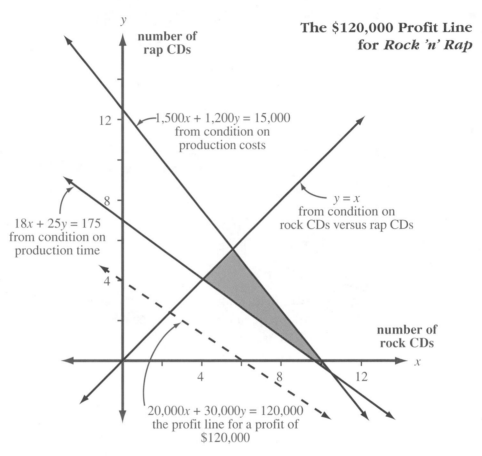

The \$120,000 Profit Line for *Rock 'n' Rap*

number of rap CDs

$1,500x + 1,200y = 15,000$ from condition on production costs

$y = x$ from condition on rock CDs versus rap CDs

$18x + 25y = 175$ from condition on production time

number of rock CDs

$20,000x + 30,000y = 120,000$ the profit line for a profit of \$120,000

"How does the profit line change as the profit increases?"

Based on a diagram like this, students should see that, as the profit increases, the profit line moves up and to the right, and last hits the feasible region at the point where the lines $y = x$ and $1,500x + 1,200y = 15,000$ intersect.

•*Finding the coordinates*

"How do you find the coordinates of the maximum profit point?"

Once students have explained where the point of maximum profit is, you can turn to their explanations of how to find the coordinates of this point. Probably some will do this graphically, by drawing careful graphs and estimating the coordinates, while others will reason it out algebraically.

For your convenience: The point of intersection has coordinates $(5\frac{5}{9}, 5\frac{5}{9})$, which students might approximate as $(5.6, 5.6)$.

Somewhere in this discussion, be sure to check that students are keeping in mind the connection between an equation and its graph. They should be aware that a point is on a graph if and only if its coordinates satisfy the equation. Thus, in the *Rock 'n' Rap* problem, the point where the lines meet has coordinates that satisfy both equations. This idea can never be mentioned too many times.

• *Check with intuition*

"How can you be sure that $(5\frac{5}{9}, 5\frac{5}{9})$ is really on both lines

At the risk of belaboring the issue, get students to articulate the fact that $(5\frac{5}{9}, 5\frac{5}{9})$ represents both of the following:

• The coordinates of the point where the lines meet.

• The common solution to the equations $y = x$ and $1{,}500x + 1{,}200y = 15{,}000$.

If students find the coordinates algebraically, they should verify that the solution also looks reasonable graphically, and vice versa.

"Is the answer reasonable in the context of the problem?"

You should also discuss the question of whether a number such as $5\frac{5}{9}$ (or 5.6) makes sense in the context of the problem. (You may need to get them to articulate that the coordinates represent the number of rock CDs and the number of rap CDs, respectively.) Their initial reaction may be that this makes no sense: You can't produce $5\frac{5}{9}$ CDs. If they say this, have them reread the problem carefully: It allows fractional production, on the grounds that it may represent beginning production one month and completing it the next month.

• *Question 3*

You might want to let students discuss Question 3 again in their groups after the preceding discussion. That would give each student a chance to review the reasoning. If time permits and you think it is worthwhile, you can ask one or more students to make a presentation also.

"How is the profit line in Question 3 different from the one in Question 2? How does this affect the solution to the problem?"

As the next diagram shows, if the profits are reversed, the profit line has a different slope, and the last point to be "hit" by a profit line is the point where the line $1{,}500x + 1{,}200y = 15{,}000$ meets the x-axis. This point has coordinates $(10, 0)$.

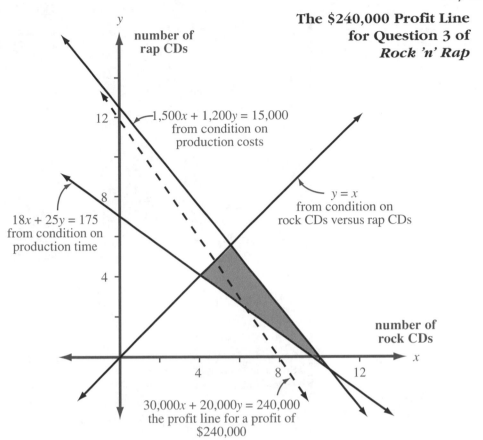

**The $240,000 Profit Line
for Question 3 of
*Rock 'n' Rap***

number of
rap CDs

$1{,}500x + 1{,}200y = 15{,}000$
from condition on
production costs

$y = x$
from condition on
rock CDs versus rap CDs

$18x + 25y = 175$
from condition on
production time

number of
rock CDs

$30{,}000x + 20{,}000y = 240{,}000$
the profit line for a profit of
$240,000

4. Optional: Homework 12: Getting on Good Terms

Note: This homework is labeled "Optional" because it is largely preparatory for the discussion on Day 13, which revolves around the use of graphing calculators to enhance student understanding. If you are not using graphing calculators with your class, you can go directly to *Homework 13: The Big U,* omitting *Homework 12: Getting on Good Terms* and Day 13. If you will be doing the graphing calculator work tomorrow, you can mention that as a motivation for this homework.

Tonight's homework accomplishes several purposes:

- It provides some algebra review.

- It focuses on the process of solving for one variable in terms of another, which students need in order to graph certain equations on the graphing calculator.

- It reinforces the meaning of equivalent equations by having students substitute solutions to one equation into an equivalent equation.

Homework 12   Getting on Good Terms

Student book page 22 →

Graphing calculators can make it easier to find feasible regions, but in order to draw the graph of an equation on a graphing calculator, the equation needs to be put into "$y =$" form.

That is, you need to write the equation so that one variable is expressed in terms of the other. For example, you might rewrite the equation $y - 5 = 4x$ as $y = 4x + 5$.

1. For each of the equations below, express the variable y in terms of the variable x:

   a. $y - 2x = 7$

   b. $7y = 14x - 21$

   c. $5x + 3y = 17$

   d. $5(x + 3y) = 2x - 3$

2. To check that you haven't made a mistake on Question 1, do the following (and show your work):

   • For each equation in Part 1, choose two values for x and then use your answers to Question 1 to find the corresponding y-values.

   • Verify that each resulting pair of values for x and y satisfies the corresponding original equation.

For example, for the sample equation $y - 5 = 4x$, suppose you choose the values $x = 3$ and $x = -1$. The sample equation has been rewritten as $y = 4x + 5$, so you substitute the x-values into this equation, getting $y = 17$ when $x = 3$ and $y = 1$ when $x = -1$.

Then you substitute each of the pairs $(3, 17)$ and $(-1, 1)$ into the original equation, $y - 5 = 4x$, to check that they fit the equation. For example, you verify that $17 - 5 = 4 \cdot 3$ is a true statement.

Optional

DAY 13

Calculator Intersections

Students see that they can use graphing calculators to draw feasible regions.

Mathematical Topics

- Solving a linear equation for one variable in terms of another
- Using graphing calculators to draw a feasible region and to estimate the coordinates of points of intersection of graphs

Outline of the Day

In Class

1. Discuss *Homework 12: Getting on Good Terms*
   - Use numerical examples to develop a general algebraic approach
2. Solve *Rock 'n' Rap* using the graphing calculator
   - Graph the equations that correspond to inequalities
   - Graph profit lines
   - Solve a variation on the problem

At Home

3. *Homework 13: The Big U*

1. Discussion of *Homework 12: Getting on Good Terms*

You might let students spend some time in their groups comparing ideas on the homework. Suggest that, if they had difficulty with any of the examples, they should try choosing a specific value to replace *x*, and try solving the resulting one-variable equation for *y*.

Then have the *diamond card* students from different groups report their results. As difficulties arise, have students use the approach just suggested. For example, in Question 1a, replacing *x* by 3 gives the equation

$$y - 2 \cdot 3 = 7$$

which students should be able to solve for *y*. A couple of such examples should give them the general solution $y = 7 + 2x$.

The process gets more difficult with each succeeding example, but the general approach should be useful in helping students.

• Graphing and checking points

Once students are sure that they have found the correct expressions for all four homework problems, have them graph each of their "*y* =" equations on the graphing calculator and check, using the trace facility on their graphing calculators, that their points from Question 2 are on the graph.

Note: The trace facility may not locate their exact point, but should give values close enough to confirm their work.

2. Solving *Rock 'n' Rap* on the Graphing Calculator

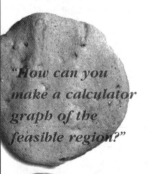

"How can you make a calculator graph of the feasible region?"

"What do the profit lines look like?"

Yesterday, students saw that the solution to the main *Rock 'n' Rap* problem was the point where the lines $1,500x + 1,200y = 15,000$ and $y = x$ intersected. They may have found the coordinates by plotting pencil-and-paper graphs or by an algebraic method. Today, students will see how to use graphing calculators, not only to find these coordinates, but also to get graphical confirmation of how the "family of parallel lines" reasoning works.

Have students begin by graphing the lines that bound the feasible region. They first have to rewrite the equations $1,500x + 1,200y = 15,000$ and $18x + 25y = 175$ in "*y* =" form in order to enter them on the graphing calculator.

They should then graph these rewritten equations and the equation $y = x$, in order to see the feasible region. Adjustments in the viewing rectangle may be needed.

Next, have students look at the parallel lines that they get for different profits. Again, they will have to rewrite the equation in "*y* =" form. For example, the profit equation $20,000x + 30,000y = 120,000$ becomes $y = (120,000 - 20,000x) \div 30,000$.

But now they have the opportunity to check out different profit lines easily simply by changing the number 120,000 in the profit line equation, and seeing what the new line looks like.

Let students play with this for a while, varying the profit and seeing how that line moves.

This should reinforce the idea that the point where the profit is greatest is at the intersection of the two lines $y = x$ and $1,500x + 1,200y = 15,000$. Then they can use the trace facility (perhaps combined with adjustments in the viewing rectangle) to get the coordinates of the desired point.

When students finish the original *Rock 'n' Rap* problem, you can ask them to work on the variation from Question 3 of the activity, in which the profits are reversed.

Suggestion: You may want to suggest to ambitious or independent students, that they see if it is possible to *shade* the feasible region on the graphing calculator. They can consult the graphing calculator manual for details.

Students at John Marshall High School in Los Angeles, CA, use calculators to find the maximum profit.

3. *Homework 13: The Big U*

This assignment is an opportunity for students to synthesize their ideas about how to solve complex problems of this type, before returning to the main unit problem, *Baker's Choice.*

Homework 13

The Big U

Student book page 23 →

Big State University has to decide how many in-state students and how many out-of-state students to admit to its next class.

These conditions are constraints on their decision:

- The college president wants this class to contribute a total of at least $2,500,000 to the school after they graduate. In the past, Big State U has received an average of $8,000 in contributions from each in-state student admitted and an average of $2,000 from each out-of-state student admitted.

- The faculty at the college want entering students with good grade-point averages. Grades of in-state students average less than grades of out-of-state students. So the faculty are urging the school to admit at least as many out-of-state students as in-state students.

- The housing office is not willing to spend more than $85,000 to cover costs (such as meals and utilities) for students in dormitories during vacation periods. Since out-of-state students are more likely to stay on campus during vacations, the housing office needs to take these differences into account. In-state students will need an average of $100 each for vacation-time costs, while out-of-state students will need an average of $200 each.

- The college treasurer wants to minimize educational costs. Because students take different courses, it costs an average of $7,200 a year to teach an in-state student and an average of $6,000 a year to teach an out-of-state student.

Your job is to recommend how many students from each category should be admitted to Big State University, based on the constraints above. Include a proof that you are minimizing costs, showing any graphs that seem helpful, and explaining your reasoning carefully.

Adapted from *An Introduction to Mathematical Models in the Social and Life Sciences*, by Michael Olinick, Addison-Wesley, 1978, p. 169.

DAY 14 Back to Cookies

Mathematical Topics

- Applying the idea of a family of parallel lines to solve a new linear programming problem
- Solving the unit problem
- Explaining the method of using a family of parallel lines to solve a linear programming problem

Outline of the Day

In Class

1. Discuss *Homework 13: The Big U*
2. *Baker's Choice Revisited*
   - Students apply concepts from the unit to the unit problem

At Home

3. *Homework 14: Reflections on Learning*

1. Discussion of Homework 13: The Big U

You might let a volunteer make a presentation on this assignment.

For your convenience: Here are the basics of the solution:

Letting x represent the number of in-state students to be admitted and y represent the number of out-of-state students, the constraints are:

$8,000x + 2,000y \geq 2,500,000$	(for contributions that the president wants)
$y \geq x$	(to satisfy the faculty's concern about grades)
$100x + 200y \leq 85,000$	(to fit the housing office's budget)
$x \geq 0, y \geq 0$	(since the values cannot be negative)

The expression to minimize (for the treasurer) is $7{,}200x + 6{,}000y$.

The first diagram below shows the graphs of the equations related to the constraints and shows the feasible region (shaded area). *Comment:* If the president had wanted a little more in contributions, or if the housing office had had a little less money, the complete set of conditions would have been impossible to fulfill.

The dotted line is from the family of parallel lines that represent different cost conditions. This particular line shows the possible combinations of enrollments that give a cost of $1,440,000; that is, the dotted line is the graph of the equation $7{,}200x + 6{,}000y = 1{,}440{,}000$. The diagram shows that the "minimum" cost line to intersect the feasible region is the one that goes through the intersection of the lines $y = x$ and $8{,}000x + 2{,}000y = 2{,}500{,}000$. Details on the reasoning follow.

The second diagram shows the shaded area in more detail and gives the coordinates of the points of intersection.

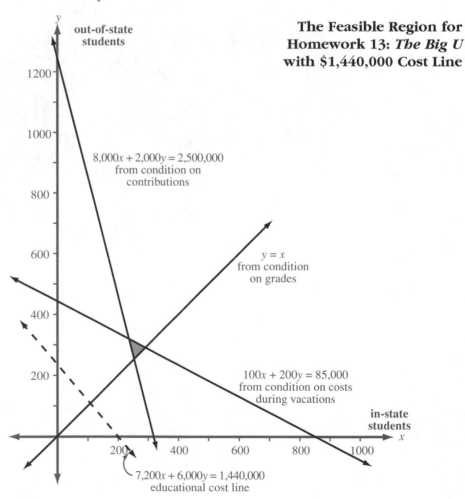

The Feasible Region for Homework 13: *The Big U* **with $1,440,000 Cost Line**

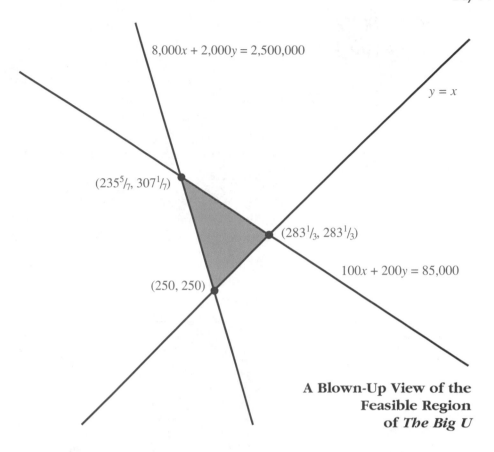

$8,000x + 2,000y = 2,500,000$

$y = x$

$(235^5/_7, 307^1/_7)$

$(283^1/_3, 283^1/_3)$

$100x + 200y = 85,000$

$(250, 250)$

**A Blown-Up View of the
Feasible Region
of *The Big U***

The point that minimizes educational costs is $(250, 250)$. Thus, the school should admit 250 in-state students and 250 out-of-state students.

In presenting the problem, students should go over how they sketched the graph, including how they knew which point minimizes the cost and how they got its coordinates.

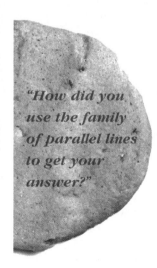

"How did you use the family of parallel lines to get your answer?"

In explaining how they identified the point, students should use the "family of parallel lines" idea, in which the combinations of in-state students and out-of-state students that give a particular cost form a straight line, and this line "slides" when the cost is changed.

Students should choose the "minimum" of this family of parallel lines. If they sketch one of these lines (for example, $7,200x + 6,000y = 1,440,000$), they will see the general direction of the lines in the family. (This is the dotted line in the first diagram.)

Students should see that the cost goes up as the line moves up and to the right, so the minimum is at the point $(250, 250)$. If students think there is ambiguity about where the "lowest" cost line intersects the feasible region, they can compute the cost at the other reasonable possibility, the point $(235 \frac{5}{7}, 307 \frac{1}{7})$, and compare the two costs.

2. *Baker's Choice Revisited*

Ask students whether they now know enough to answer the original *Baker's Choice* question. Have them look at the new activity on this problem, called *Baker's Choice Revisited*. Point out that the problem itself is unchanged, and have them carefully look over the part called "Your Assignment." Emphasize that you want a good written presentation of their reasoning.

We suggest that you give groups the rest of today's class and some of tomorrow's to produce these reports, with presentations at the end of tomorrow's class. Although students should work with their groups on this activity, it is important that students do individual write-ups for inclusion in their unit portfolios.

You may want to remind the class that they did considerable work on Days 1–8 toward solving this problem. They can use that earlier work as help, but their reports should explain everything from scratch.

Student book page 24 →

Baker's Choice Revisited

Abby and Bing Woo have a small bakery shop that specializes in cookies.

They make only two kinds of cookies—plain cookies and cookies with icing. They need to decide *how many dozens* of each kind of cookies to make for tomorrow.

One dozen of their *plain* cookies requires one pound of cookie dough (and no icing), while one dozen of their *iced* cookies requires 0.7 pounds of cookie dough and 0.4 pounds of icing.

The Woos know from experience that each dozen of the plain cookies requires about 0.1 hours of preparation time, and each dozen of the iced cookies requires about 0.15 hours of preparation time.

They also know that, no matter how many of each kind they make, they will be able to sell them all.

Their decision is limited by the following things:

- The ingredients they have on hand—they have 110 pounds of cookie dough and 32 pounds of icing.
- The amount of oven space available—they have room to bake a total of 140 dozen cookies for tomorrow.
- The amount of preparation time available—together they have 15 hours for cookie preparation.

Why should the Woos care how many cookies of each kind they make? You guessed it! They want to make as much money as possible. They sell the plain cookies for $6.00 a dozen and it costs them $4.50 a dozen to make those cookies. The iced cookies sell for $7.00 a dozen and cost $5.00 a dozen to make.

The Big Question is:

How many dozens of each kind of cookie should the Woos make so that their profit is as high as possible?

Continued on next page

Continued from previous page

▶ *Your Assignment*
▶
▶ Pretend that your group is a business consulting team. The Woos have come to you for help. Not
▶ only should you give them an answer, but you should explain to them clearly how you know that
▶ you have the best possible answer so that they will pick your group in the future when they
▶ need help.

Student book page 25 →

▶ You may want to review what you already know from earlier work on this problem. Look at your
▶ notes and earlier assignments.

▶ Then write a report for the Woos. Your report should include the following:

▶   • An answer to the Woos' dilemma, including a summary of how much cookie dough, icing,
▶   preparation time, and oven time they will use.

▶   • An explanation for the Woos that will convince them that your answer gives them the
▶   most profit.

▶   • Any graphs, charts, equations, or diagrams that are needed as part of your explanation.

▶ You should write your report based on the assumption that the Woos do not know the
▶ techniques you have learned in this unit about solving this type of problem.

▶ ▲ ▲ ▲ ▲ ▲ ▲ ▲ ▲

3. *Homework 14: Reflections on Learning*

This assignment gives students an opportunity to compare the type of learning in this unit to their previous experiences studying mathematics.

Student book page 25 →

Homework 14   Reflections on Learning

Now that you are almost at the end of *Baker's Choice,* it's time
to reflect on your experience with this unit of mathematics.

1. How has your experience working on *Baker's Choice*
   been different from your previous experiences
   learning mathematics? Include differences in the way
   you learned as well as differences in the way the
   mathematics was presented.

2. Describe your own feelings about this type of
   learning. Include issues such as the following:

   • How well did you understand the mathematics?

   • How much did you enjoy the experience?

   • How did the experience affect your perceptions
     and attitudes about other students in the class?

[The problems in Baker's Choice*] represented situations that I could see myself in*

in the future.

Nicole, Student
Homework 14: Reflections on Learning

Kalaid Azar, Jarrod Young, and Ryan Bauer work on Homework 13: The Big U, and discover that cost lines, like profit lines, form a parallel family.

DAY 15 *Finishing Cookies*

Students make final presentations on the unit problem.

Mathematical Topics

- Explaining the method of using a family of parallel lines to solve a linear programming problem
- Solving the unit problem

Outline of the Day

In Class

1. Discuss *Homework 14: Reflections on Learning*
2. Provide additional time as needed for students to finish work on *Baker's Choice Revisited* (from Day 14)
3. Presentations of *Baker's Choice Revisited*

At Home

4. *Homework 15: Beginning Portfolio Selection*

1. Discussion of *Homework 14: Reflections on Learning*

You can have students share ideas in their groups while you check off who has done the homework. You may want to collect this assignment to get a sense of how the students felt about the unit.

2. Continued Work on *Baker's Choice Revisited*

It is hard to predict how much time students will need to finish their work on this problem and to prepare reports.

If you think that doing the reports today is not feasible, you can postpone them until tomorrow.

3. Presentations of *Baker's Choice Revisited*

Let one or two groups present their analysis of the *Baker's Choice* problem. The following graph is the same as the graph of the feasible region given on Day 8, except that one of the profit lines has been added (represented by the dotted line). This line is the graph of the equation $1.5x + 2y = 150$ and shows the combinations of dozens of plain cookies (x) and dozens of iced cookies (y) which will give a total profit of $150.

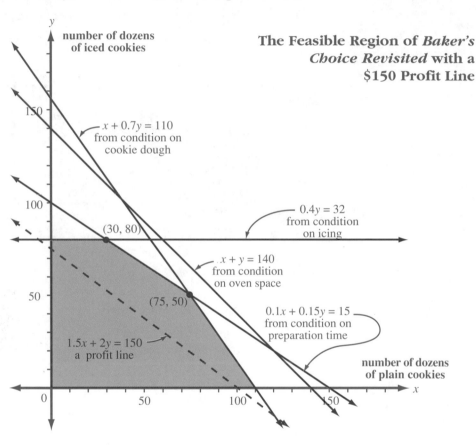

y

number of dozens of iced cookies

The Feasible Region of *Baker's Choice Revisited* with a $150 Profit Line

$x + 0.7y = 110$
from condition on cookie dough

$0.4y = 32$
from condition on icing

(30, 80)

$x + y = 140$
from condition on oven space

$1.5x + 2y = 150$
a profit line

(75, 50)

$0.1x + 0.15y = 15$
from condition on preparation time

number of dozens of plain cookies

Some questions you can ask if presentations don't deal with them:
"What does each line represent?"
"How do you determine the shaded area?"
"What expression describes profit?"
"Why is (75, 50) the best choice?"

At this stage in their understanding of the problem, students should definitely include the coordinates of the key points shown—(30, 80) and (75, 50). They should be able to explain what each of the lines represents and how the shaded area is determined. For example, they should be able to explain why we take the area *below* rather than the area *above* a certain line.

Finally, they should identify the expression $1.5x + 2y$ as describing the profit and be able to explain why the best choice for the Woos is to make 75 dozen plain cookies and 50 dozen iced cookies.

They will probably use the "family of parallel lines" reasoning, explaining that the points that give a particular profit are on a straight line and that, as the desired profit increases, the line is replaced by one parallel to it which is above and to the right of the one before. The last of these lines to intersect the region is the one through the point (75, 50).

You can ask how they can be sure where the "parallel family" leaves the region. For example, how do they know it isn't at the point (30, 80)? Students might respond by saying that the answer must be at either (30, 80) or (75, 50), because these are corners, and then just evaluate the profit expression $1.5x + 2y$ at both points to see which is better. The profit at (30, 80) is $205, while the profit at (75, 50) is $212.50.

4. *Homework 15: Beginning Portfolio Selection*

This assignment gets students started on compiling their portfolios for this unit, asking them to think about a specific aspect of the mathematics developed in the unit.

Before assigning this homework, you might discuss with students what portfolios are and how they are used in the world. For instance, you can discuss examples such as artists' portfolios to illustrate the general idea.

The portfolios for this unit will serve two purposes:

• The process of assembling the portfolio will make students reflect on what they have learned, thus deepening the learning.

• The work that goes in the portfolio will represent what students have learned and the quality of their work to their parents, future teachers, or potential employers.

• •

To solve these kind of problems, make up equations out of the given constraints and graph them. Then find the feasible region and shade it. The next step is to make a profit line. To make this line state the profit equation equal to any number and graph it. As all the profit lines are parallel the number the profit equation is equaled doesn't matter. Using a straightedge now slide it upwards or downwards parallel to the profit line and find the points where the results are minimum and where it is maximum, then if the question asks for maximum give the maximum answer and if it asks for minimum then give the minimum answer. Don't forget to shade your feasibility region as the maximum point is the point where the profit line touches the feasible region the last and the minimum is where the profit line touches the feasible region the first.

J.D. Hogan, Student
Homework 15: Beginning Portfolio Selection

Homework 15 Beginning Portfolio Selection

Student book page 26 →

The main problem for this unit, *Baker's Choice,* is an example of a **linear programming** problem. You have seen several such problems, including the situations in the following activities:

- *Homework 8: Picturing Pictures*
- *Homework 10: You Are What You Eat*
- *Rock 'n' Rap*
- *Homework 13: The Big U*

1. Describe the steps you must go through to solve such a problem.

2. Pick three activities from the unit that helped you understand particular steps of this process. Explain how each activity helped you understand the process. (You do not need to restrict yourself to the activities listed above.)

Note: Selecting activities and writing the accompanying explanations are the first steps toward compiling your portfolio for this unit.

DAY 16

Students reflect on the unit and compile key pieces of the work into a portfolio.

Baker's Choice Portfolio

Mathematical Topics

- Compiling unit portfolios
- Reflecting on the unit

Outline of the Day

In Class

1. Discuss *Homework 15: Beginning Portfolio Selection*
   - Introduce the term **linear programming**
2. *Baker's Choice Portfolio*
   - Students write cover letters and finish selecting materials to include in their portfolios

At Home

3. No written homework (Students prepare for unit assessments)

1. Discussion of Homework 15: Beginning Portfolio Selection

You can have a couple of volunteers read their descriptions of the overall process for solving linear programming problems. You may want to discuss the term *linear programming* and bring out why the term *linear* is used. You may also want to discuss what makes a good description.

You may also want to have some students share their choice of activities in Part 2 of the assignment and their explanations of how these activities helped them.

You may also want to share some of the following general background information about linear programming.

- *For teachers: Background about linear programming*

In general, a **linear programming** problem is a problem whose goal is to minimize or maximize a linear expression in certain variables, subject to a set of constraints. These constraints are linear inequalities or equations involving those variables. Such problems occur constantly in everyday business settings.

The linear programming problems that students did in this unit are the most elementary type, primarily because they involve only two variables and only a small number of constraints.

For more complex problems, the task of finding the right vertex is vastly more complicated. In many applications, the problems are solvable only with super-computers, and with the help of techniques that help search for the right vertex.

The best known of these techniques is the *simplex method,* invented in the early 1950s. Credit for inventing this technique is generally given to George Dantzig, a professor of operations research and computer science at Stanford University.

The simplex method and other techniques are widely used today in many industries to solve linear programming problems that may involve hundreds or thousands of variables.

2. Baker's Choice Portfolio

"What is an artist's portfolio? What is a mathematician's portfolio?"

Students should now add to the material they selected last night, using the instructions that follow. If this is their first experience writing about their

After looking over her work on **Baker's Choice,** *student Irma Garcia is assembling her portfolio.*

work, you may want to look at their initial efforts and then give them a chance to rewrite.

While Students Are Working

▼ ▼

If students need some prompting to get going on their cover letters, you can suggest that they begin by restating the unit problem in their own words.

They can also use last night's homework as a guide, and look for the mathematical ideas used in each step of the process.

Student book page 27 →

Baker's Choice Portfolio

Now that *Baker's Choice* is completed, it is time to put together your portfolio for the unit. This has three parts:
• Writing a cover letter summarizing the unit.
• Choosing papers to include from your work in this unit.
• Discussing your personal growth during the unit.

Cover Letter for Baker's Choice

Look back over *Baker's Choice* and describe the central problem of the unit and the main mathematical ideas. Your description should give an overview of how the key ideas were developed in this unit and how you used them to solve the central problem.

Selecting Papers from Baker's Choice

Your portfolio from *Baker's Choice* should contain the following items:
   • *Homework 15: Beginning Portfolio Selection*
      Include the activities from the unit that you selected in *Homework 15: Beginning Portfolio Selection* along with your written work about those activities.
   • A Problem of the Week
      Select one of the two POWs you completed during this unit (*The Broken Eggs* or *Kick It!*).
   • Other quality work
      Select one or two other pieces of work that demonstrate your best efforts. (These can be any work from the unit—Problem of the Week, homework, classwork, presentation, and so on.)
   • *Baker's Choice Revisited*
      Include your report from this problem.
   • Later you will add the In-Class and Take-Home Assessments for *Baker's Choice*.

Personal Growth

Your cover letter for *Baker's Choice* describes how the unit develops. As part of your portfolio, write about your own development during this unit. You may want to address the following:
   • How you feel you progressed in areas of:
      —working together with others
      —presenting to the class
      —writing about and describing your thought processes
   • What you feel that you need to work on and how you might work on it.

You should include here any other thoughts about your experience with this unit that you want to share with a reader of your portfolio.   ▲ ▲ ▲ ▲ ▲ ▲ ▲ ▲

3. No Written Homework

Students' homework for tonight is to prepare for tomorrow's unit assessments by reviewing the ideas of the unit.

• •

[Baker's Choice] was set up in a way that let me picture what was going on. I understood it much better than I have understood other units in math. I also like the way that each night we had one big problem instead of a bunch of shorter problems. The POWs were good because I don't usually get to work on problem[s] that are that involved. This experience made it easier for me to work with other students in my class. I also got to see other views of problems from them.

Laura Scott, Student
Homework 14: Reflections on Learning

Assessments

Students do the in-class assessment and can begin the take-home assessment.

Special Materials Needed

- In-Class Assessment for *Baker's Choice*
- Take-Home Assessment for *Baker's Choice*

Outline of the Day

In Class

1. Introduce assessments
2. Students do *In-Class Assessment for Baker's Choice*
3. Students begin *Take-Home Assessment for Baker's Choice*

At Home

4. Students complete *Take-Home Assessment for Baker's Choice*

1. Introducing the Assessments

Tell students that today they will get two tests—one that they finish in class and one that they can start in class and will finish at home. The take-home part should be handed in tomorrow.

Tell students that they are allowed to use graphing calculators, notes from previous work, and so on, in their work on the assessment. (They will probably have to do without the graphing calculators on the take-home portion.)

2. In-Class Assessment for Baker's Choice

Students should work individually on the in-class assessment.

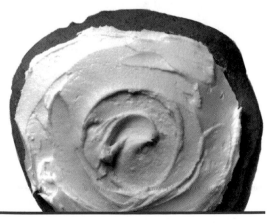

Not in student book →

In-Class Assessment for Baker's Choice

The problems in this assessment are variations on the *Baker's Choice* problem of the Woos. In each problem, you are to find the combination of plain and iced cookies that maximizes the Woos' profit for the new situation and explain your answer. Consider these three variations from the original situation *as three separate problems*.

Each problem is accompanied by a graph that shows the feasible region of the original problem, with the shaded area representing that original feasible region.

Problems 1 and 2 show a profit line based on the original problem. Problem 3 shows a profit line based on a different profit expression. The other lines shown in each case are the graphs of the equations corresponding to the original problem's constraint inequalities. These inequalities are as follows:

$$x + y \leq 140 \qquad \text{(for the amount of oven space)}$$

$$x + 0.7y \leq 110 \qquad \text{(for the amount of cookie dough)}$$

$$0.4y \leq 32 \qquad \text{(for the amount of icing)}$$

$$0.1x + 0.15y \leq 15 \qquad \text{(for the amount of the Woos'} \\ \text{preparation time)}$$

In-Class Assessment for Baker's Choice

1. Suppose everything is the same as the original problem, *except* that the Woos have an *unlimited amount of cookie dough*. What combination of plain and iced cookies should the Woos make to maximize their profit?

Not in student book →

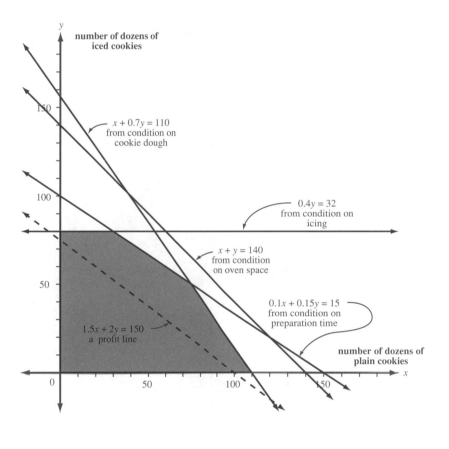

number of dozens of
iced cookies

$x + 0.7y = 110$
from condition on
cookie dough

$0.4y = 32$
from condition on
icing

$x + y = 140$
from condition
on oven space

$0.1x + 0.15y = 15$
from condition on
preparation time

number of dozens of
plain cookies

$1.5x + 2y = 150$
a profit line

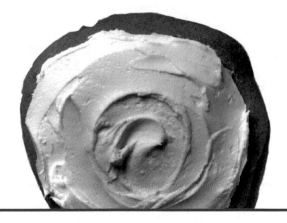

In-Class Assessment for Baker's Choice

2. Suppose everything is the same as the original problem, *except* that the Woos have the additional constraint that they can't sell more than 60 dozen plain cookies. What combination of plain and iced cookies should the Woos make to maximize their profit?

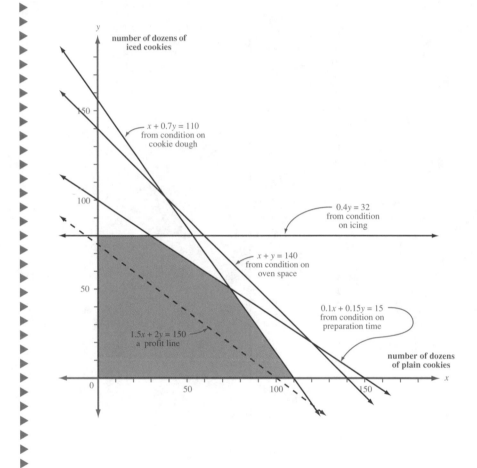

y

number of dozens of iced cookies

150

x + 0.7*y* = 110
from condition on
cookie dough

100

0.4*y* = 32
from condition
on icing

x + *y* = 140
from condition on
oven space

50

0.1*x* + 0.15*y* = 15
from condition on
preparation time

1.5*x* + 2*y* = 150
a profit line

**number of dozens
of plain cookies**

0   50   100   150   *x*

3. Suppose everything is the same as the original problem, *except* that the Woos make a profit of $2 on each dozen plain cookies and $4 on each dozen iced cookies (instead of the original profits of $1.50 and $2). What combination of plain and iced cookies should the Woos make to maximize their profit?

Not in student book →

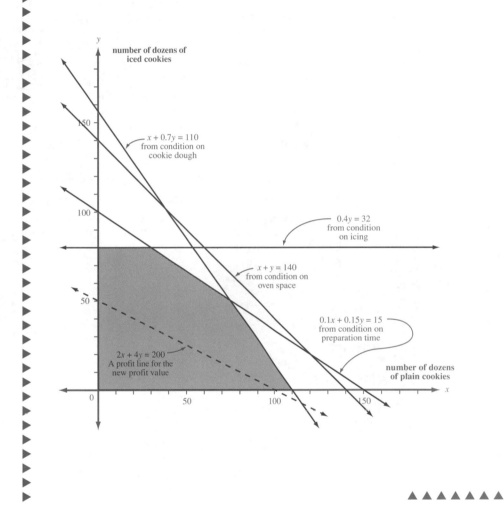

3. *Take-Home Assessment for Baker's Choice*

As students finish the in-class assessment, they can begin work on the take-home assessment.

Take-Home Assessment for *Baker's Choice*

Not in student book →

Linda Sue is a stunt pilot, but she found that she can't make a living doing stunts. So she has bought a transport plane from her friend Philip. He agrees to help her set up her business.

He has two customers he no longer has time to serve and suggests that she work for them, delivering their merchandise.

Charley's Chicken Feed packages its product in containers that weigh 40 pounds and are 2 cubic feet in volume. Philip has been charging them $2.20 a container.

Careful Calculators packages its materials in cartons that weigh 50 pounds ans are 3 cubic feet in volume. Philip has been charging them $3.00 a carton.

The plane can hold a maximum volume of 2,000 cubic feet of cargo and it can carry a maximum weight of 37,000 pounds.

Both *Charley's Chicken Feed* and *Careful Calculators* told Linda that she can have as much business as she can handle, and the same flight route serves both customers' needs. Of course, Linda Sue wants to maximize the money she gets per flight, so she can spend more time on stunt flying.

Here are your tasks:

1. Use variables and algebra to describe the constraints on what Linda Sue can carry.

2. Sketch the feasible region for Linda Sue's situation.

3. Find the combination of chicken feed and calculators that Linda Sue should carry in order to maximize her income. (Assume that Linda Sue charges the same rates that Philip did.)

4. Homework: Complete *Take-Home Assessment for Baker's Choice*

Students should bring back the completed assessment tomorrow. As with a work at home, students may collaborate or get assistance, but they should report this as part of their write-up of the assessment.

DAY 18 Summing Up

Students sum up what they've learned.

Mathematical Topic

• Summarizing the unit

Outline of the Day

In Class
1. Discuss unit assessments
2. Sum up the unit

1. Discussion of the Unit Assessments

You can have students volunteer to explain their work on each of the problems. Encourage questions and alternative explanations from other students.

2. Unit Summary

You can let students share their portfolio cover letters as a way to start a discussion summarizing the unit.

You can let them brainstorm ideas they have learned in this unit, perhaps including a list of new terms (such as *feasible region* or *constraint*) or ideas they used in a new context (such as *parallel lines* or *equivalence*).

This is a good opportunity to place this unit in a broader mathematics context. For example, you can ask what class they think this unit belongs in. You can bring out that the graphing ideas used in the unit involve a combination of algebra and geometry.

Appendix

Supplemental Problems

This appendix contains five additional activities that you can use to supplement the regular material of the unit.

More Broken Eggs

This activity asks students to look for the general solution to the problem from *POW 1: The Broken Eggs.*

Hassan's a Hit!

This problem is a variation on the situation from *Profitable Pictures* (on Day 9) in which the profit amounts for each type of picture have changed (as in Problem 2 of *Homework 9: Curtis and Hassan Make Choices*). The purpose of this activity is for students to see that the maximum is not always at the same point, even if the feasible region is the same.

Get the Point?

You can use this activity to get students to discover (or rediscover) the substitution method for solving two linear equations in two variables.

Charity Rock

This problem presents an interesting context in which students set up and solve a system of linear equations. If you spend a day working on techniques to solve pairs of linear equations, this activity would be good homework.

Producing Programming Problems

This problem is an excellent group activity to deepen students' understanding of linear programming. You should use it at the end of the unit.

Student book page 28 →

▼▼▼▼▼▼▼▼▼▼▼▼▼▼▼▼▼▼▼▼▼▼▼▼▼▼▼▼▼▼▼▼▼▼▼

More Broken Eggs

In *POW 1: The Broken Eggs,* you found a number of eggs that the farmer might possibly have had when her cart was knocked over.

You may have found only one solution to that problem, but there are actually many solutions.

Your task on this problem is to look for other solutions to the problem. Find as many as you can. If possible, find and describe a pattern for getting all the solutions and explain why all solutions fit your pattern.

Here are the facts you need to know:

- When the farmer put the eggs in groups of two, there was one egg left over.

- When she put them in groups of three, there was also one egg left over. The same thing happened when she put them in groups of four, five, or six.

- When she put the eggs in groups of seven, she ended up with complete groups of seven with no eggs left over.

▲▲▲▲▲▲▲▲

Student book page 29 →

▼▼▼▼▼▼▼▼▼▼▼▼▼▼▼▼▼▼▼▼▼▼▼▼▼▼▼▼▼▼▼▼▼▼▼▼▼▼

Hassan's a Hit!

Hassan's pictures are indeed a big hit, especially the watercolors. Based on his success, he is raising his prices as he planned in *Homework 9: Curtis and Hassan Make Choices.*

That is, he will now make a profit of $50 on each pastel and a profit of $175 on each watercolor.

Assume that he will still have the same constraints. That is, he will still have only $180 to spend on materials and will still be able to make at most 16 pictures.

He had already figured out, with the previous prices, how many he should make of each type of picture to maximize his overall profit.

If he still wants to maximize his overall profit, with the new prices, should he now change the number of pictures he makes of each type? Explain your answer.

▲▲▲▲▲▲▲▲

Get the Point?

Student book page 30 →

In solving problems like the cookie problem, it is helpful to know how to find the point where two lines intersect.

Your group's goal in this activity is to discover a method of doing this, besides guessing or using graphs, by working with the equations of the two straight lines.

Your written report on the activity should include the following:

- • Solutions to Questions 1a–1e.

- • Two of the problems made up for Question 2 by individual group members, with solutions.

- • Your group's written directions for Question 3.

1. For each of the following pairs of equations, find the point of intersection of their graphs by a method other than graphing or trial and error. When you think you have each solution, check it by graphing or by substituting the values into the pair of equations.

   a. $y = x$ and $3x = y + 4$

   b. $y = 2x + 5$ and $y = 3x - 7$

   c. $3x + 2y = 13$ and $y = 4x + 1$

   d. $7x - 3y = 31$ and $y - 5 = 3x$

   e. $x + 3y = 17$ and $2y + 1 = 3x$

2. Each person in the group should make up a pair of linear equations, and find the point of intersection. Then group members should trade problems (without giving solutions) and work on each other's problems, trying to find the point of intersection without guessing or graphing.

3. As a group, develop and write down general directions for finding the coordinates of the point of intersection of two equations for straight lines without guessing or graphing. Make your directions easy to follow, so someone in middle school could use them to "get the point."

▲ ▲ ▲ ▲ ▲ ▲ ▲

▼▼▼▼▼▼▼▼▼▼▼▼▼▼▼▼▼▼▼▼▼▼▼▼▼▼▼▼▼▼▼▼▼▼▼▼▼▼

A Charity Rock

Student book page 31 →

At concerts given by the group *Rocking Pebbles,* some of the tickets are for reserved seats, and the rest are general admission.

For a recent *Rocking Pebbles* series of two weekend concerts, the *Pebbles* pledged to give half of the proceeds they got from the general admission tickets to charity. After the concerts, the charity called the *Pebbles'* manager to find out how much money the charity would get.

The manager looked up the records and found that, for the first night, 230 reserved seat tickets and 835 general admission tickets were sold. For the second night, 250 reserved seat tickets and 980 general admission tickets were sold. The manager saw that the total amount of money collected for tickets was $23,600 for the first night and $27,100 for the second night, but she didn't know the prices for the two different kinds of tickets. (The prices were the same at both concerts.)

Could you help the manager by figuring out how much the *Pebbles* will give to charity? While you're at it, figure out what the two ticket prices were.

▲ ▲ ▲ ▲ ▲ ▲ ▲ ▲

▼▼▼▼▼▼▼▼▼▼▼▼▼▼▼▼▼▼▼▼▼▼▼▼▼▼▼▼▼▼▼▼▼▼▼▼▼▼

Producing Programming Problems

Student book page 32 →

Your group is to make up a linear programming problem. The key ingredients you need to have in your problem are

- two variables,
- a *linear expression* using those variables to be maximized or minimized, and
- three or four *linear constraints.*

Once you have written your problem, you must solve it.

Then you prepare an *interesting* 5 to 10 minute presentation with the overhead projector which

- explains the problem,
- provides a solution of the problem, and
- proves there is no better solution.

▲ ▲ ▲ ▲ ▲ ▲ ▲ ▲

Student Materials

Blackline Masters

Baker's Choice

Abby and Bing Woo have a small bakery shop that specializes in cookies.

They make only two kinds of cookies—plain cookies and cookies with icing. They need to decide *how many dozens* of each kind of cookies to make for tomorrow.

One dozen of their *plain* cookies requires a pound of cookie dough (and no icing), while one dozen of their *iced* cookies requires 0.7 pounds of cookie dough and 0.4 pounds of icing.

The Woos know from experience that each dozen of the plain cookies requires about 0.1 hours of preparation time, and each dozen of the iced cookies requires about 0.15 hours of preparation time.

They also know that, no matter how many of each kind they make, they will be able to sell them all.

Their decision is limited by the following things:

- The ingredients they have on hand—they have 110 pounds of cookie dough and 32 pounds of icing.

- The amount of oven space available—they have room to bake a total of 140 dozen cookies for tomorrow.

- The amount of preparation time available—together they have 15 hours for cookie preparation.

Why on earth should the Woos care how many cookies of each kind they make? Well, you guessed it! They want to make as much money as possible. They sell the plain cookies for $6.00 a dozen and it costs them $4.50 a dozen to make those cookies. The iced cookies sell for $7.00 a dozen and cost $5.00 a dozen to make.

The Big Question is:

How many dozens of each kind of cookie should Abby and Bing make so that their profit is as high as possible?

1. a. To begin answering the Big Question, find one combination of plain cookies and iced cookies that will satisfy all of the conditions in the problem.

    b. Find out how much profit the Woos will make on that combination of cookies.

2. Now find a different combination of cookies that fits the problem, but that makes a greater profit for the Woos.

This problem was adapted from one in *Introduction to Linear Programming,* 2nd Edition, by R. Stansbury Stockton, Allyn and Bacon, 1963, pp. 19-35.

Homework 1   A Simpler Cookie

The Woos have a rather complicated problem to solve. Let's make it simpler. Finding a solution to a simpler problem may lead to a method for solving the original problem.

Assume that the Woos still make plain cookies and cookies with icing. Also assume that they still have 15 hours altogether for cookie preparation.

But now assume that they have an unlimited amount of both cookie dough and icing and that they have an unlimited amount of space in their oven.

The other information is unchanged, and is as follows:

- Preparing a dozen plain cookies requires 0.1 hours.

- Preparing a dozen iced cookies requires 0.15 hours.

- They sell the plain cookies for $6.00 a dozen.

- It costs them $4.50 a dozen to make plain cookies.

- They sell the iced cookies for $7.00 a dozen.

- It costs them $5.00 a dozen to make iced cookies.

As before, the Woos know that no matter how many of each kind they make, they will be able to sell them all.

1. Find at least five combinations of plain and of iced cookies that the Woos could make without working more than 15 hours. For each combination, find the profit that they would make.

2. Find the combination of plain and iced cookies that you think would give the Woos the greatest profit. Explain why you think no other combination will give a greater profit.

POW 1 — *The Broken Eggs*

A farmer is taking her eggs to market in her cart, but she hits a pot-hole, which knocks over all the containers of eggs.

Though she herself is unhurt, every egg is broken.

So she goes to her insurance agent, who asks her how many eggs she had. She says she doesn't know, but she remembers some things from various ways she tried packing the eggs.

She knows that when she put the eggs in groups of two, there was one egg left over. When she put them in groups of three, there was also one egg left over. The same thing happened when she put them in groups of four, groups of five, or groups of six.

But when she put them in groups of seven, she ended up with complete groups of seven with no eggs left over.

Your task is to answer the following question:

What can the farmer figure out from this information about how many eggs she had? Is there more than one possibility?

Write-up

You should write up your work on this problem using the following categories:

1. *Process:* Based on your notes, describe what you did in attempting to solve this problem. You might want to talk about such things as approaches you tried that didn't work, what you did when you got stuck, who you talked to and any ideas you got from them, and so on.

2. *Results:*

   a. State your results on the problem as clearly as you can. (If you only obtained a partial solution, give that.) Include any insights you had other than numerical solutions.

   b. Explain how you know that your answer (or partial answer) is correct. Your explanation should be written in a way that will be convincing to someone else— even someone who initially disagrees with your answer.

Homework 2

High School Letters

The list below uses certain symbols or symbol combinations as variables to represent certain quantities concerning a particular high school.

For example, C stands for the number of classes each student takes at that high school; G_9 stands for the number of 9th grade girls at the school.

You may want to think of some of the numerical values as representing the average for the appropriate group of students.

symbol	meaning	numerical value
C	the number of classes taken by each student	5
G_9	the number of 9th grade girls	230
B_9	the number of 9th grade boys	246
G_{10}	the number of 10th grade girls	215
B_{10}	the number of 10th grade boys	213
G_{11}	the number of 11th grade girls	189
B_{11}	the number of 11th grade boys	198
G_{12}	the number of 12th grade girls	178
B_{12}	the number of 12th grade boys	183
H_M	the number of minutes each student spends on math homework each night	27
H_O	the number of minutes each student spends on homework other than math each night	52
M	the number of minutes each class lasts	50
D	the number of class days a year	180
L_G	the number of hours a week each girl student listens to music	18
L_B	the number of hours a week each boy student listens to music	15

Using the symbols above, it is possible to write many different algebraic expressions. Although you can always substitute numbers and do the arithmetic, most of these expressions have no real meaning in the situation.

For example, consider the expression DL_G. Certainly you can multiply "the number of class days a year" (180) by "the number of hours a week each girl student listens to music" (18), but the product you get (3,240) doesn't have any interpretation in terms of the problem. In other words, DL_G doesn't really mean anything.

However, some expressions *do* have a meaning. For example, in the expression $H_M + H_O$, each term represents part of a student's homework time. The sum represents the total number of minutes each student spends on homework each night. So the expression $H_M + H_O$ is meaningful in the situation.

The phrase "the total number of minutes each student spends on homework each night" is a concise way to describe the number represented by $H_M + H_O$. We will call this concise description the **summary phrase** for the expression.

The list above tells us that each student spends 27 minutes on math homework, so $H_M = 27$, and that each student spends 52 minutes on other homework, so $H_O = 52$.

Therefore, $H_M + H_O = 27 + 52 = 79$, so each student spends 79 minutes a night on homework. But even if the numbers were different, $H_M + H_O$ would still represent the number of minutes each student spends on homework each night.

Your Task

Your task is to come up with as many *meaningful* algebraic expressions as you can, using the symbols above. For each expression, do each of the following:

- Write the expression.

- Explain what the expression means, using a summary phrase.

- Give the numerical value of the expression, based on the values of the individual variables given in the chart.

• • • • • • • • • • • • • • •

Investigating Inequalities

You know that two equations are called **equivalent** if they have the same solutions. For example, the equation $2x + 5 = 8$ is equivalent to the equation $2x = 3$, since the equations have the same solution, $x = 1.5$.

You have also learned some techniques for creating equivalent equations. For example, you can get the equation $2x = 3$ from the equation $2x + 5 = 8$ by subtracting 5 from both sides.

Equivalent inequalities are similar to equivalent equations. Two inequalities are also called **equivalent** if they have the same solutions.

The concept is more complicated for inequalities, since an inequality usually has infinitely many solutions, while an equation often has only one solution. So keep in mind that, for two inequalities to be equivalent, *every solution* of each must also be a solution of the other.

Your task in this activity is to investigate whether the standard techniques for getting equivalent *equations* can also be used to produce equivalent *inequalities.*

You can start by working with the inequality $4x \leq 20$, and finding some numbers that satisfy this inequality.

Then try doing each of the following operations to the inequality $4x \leq 20$ to produce new inequalities:

• Add the same number to both sides of the inequality.

• Subtract the same number from both sides of the inequality.

• Multiply both sides of the inequality by the same non-zero number.

• Divide both sides of the inequality by the same non-zero number.

For each operation, do at least one example where "the same number" is *positive* and at least one where "the same number" is *negative*.

For each new inequality you create, decide whether the numbers that satisfy the new inequality are the same as those that satisfy the original inequality. In other words, investigate whether doing each of the operations to the inequality $4x \leq 20$ will produce an equivalent inequality.

Also think about what would happen if you started with a different inequality.

When you have completed your investigation, summarize your conclusions about working with inequalities.

Homework 3 Variables of Your Own

1. Make up a set of between 5 and 10 variables for a situation, similar to the list in *Homework 2: High School Letters*.

   For instance, you might call your situation Marching Band, Letters, Baseball Game Letters, Party Letters, or Clothing Store Letters. If you prefer, you can make up a situation of your own.

2. On the front side of your homework paper, write three expressions using your variables for which someone can write a summary phrase. On the back side, write the summary phrase.

3. On the front side of your homework paper, write three summary phrases for which someone can write an algebraic expression using your variables. On the back side, write the expression.

In the next class, you will exchange papers with other students and see if you can figure out the summary phrases and algebraic expressions for each other's situations.

Picturing Cookies —Part I

By graphing relationships, we can turn symbolic relationships into geometric ones.

Since geometric relationships are visual, they are often easier to think about than algebraic statements.

One of the constraints in *Baker's Choice* is that the Woos can use at most 110 pounds of cookie dough. You can represent this constraint symbolically by the inequality $x + 0.7y \leq 110$, where x is the number of dozens of plain cookies and y is the number of dozens of iced cookies.

Choose one color to use for combinations of plain and iced cookies that satisfy the constraint. In other words, this color is for combinations that use 110 pounds or less of cookie dough. Choose a different color for combinations that do not satisfy the constraint, that is, for combinations that use more than 110 pounds of cookie dough.

For instance, 20 dozen plain cookies and 50 dozen iced cookies is a combination that satisfies the constraint, since this combination uses $20 + 0.7 \cdot 50$ pounds of cookie dough, for a total of only 55 pounds. That is, "$20 + 0.7 \cdot 50 \leq 110$" is a true statement. So the first color should be used for the point (20, 50).

But 100 dozen of each type of cookie does not satisfy the constraint, since this combination uses $100 + 0.7 \cdot 100$ pounds of cookie dough, for a total of 170 pounds. That is, the statement "$100 + 0.7 \cdot 100 \leq 110$" is not true. So the second color should be used for the point (100, 100).

Your task is to create a diagram showing both types of points, and then describe the graph of the inequality itself. (The graph of the inequality consists of all points that fit the constraint, that is, points of the first color.)

Steps 1–4 give details about what you need to do. Do your final diagram on a sheet of grid chart paper. If you have time, do Question 5, dealing with other constraints.

1. Each person in the group should try many pairs of numbers for the variables, testing whether or not each pair satisfies the constraint. *On one shared set of coordinate axes,* group members should each mark their number pairs using the appropriate color.

2. Make sure that your group has points of both colors. After some experimentation, you may need to change the scale on your axes so that you can show both types of points. If necessary, redraw your diagram with a new scale and replot the points that you have already found.

3. Continue with Parts 1 and 2, adding points of each type in the appropriate color. Keep plotting points until you get the "big picture," that is, until you are sure what the overall diagram looks like.

4. Include with your final diagram a statement explaining what you think the graph of the inequality itself looks like and why.

5. Repeat the process used in Parts 1–4 or use the "big picture" to graph the remaining constraints, each on its own set of axes.

Homework 4 Inequality Stories

You have seen that certain real-world situations can be described using inequalities.

In the *Baker's Choice* problem, for example, each dozen plain cookies uses one pound of cookie dough and each dozen iced cookies uses 0.7 pounds of cookie dough, but the Woos have only 110 pounds of cookie dough.

This limitation can be described by the "cookie dough inequality" $x + 0.7y \leq 110$, where x is the number of dozens of plain cookies and y is the number of dozens of iced cookies.

In this assignment, you will look more at the relationship between real-world situations and inequalities.

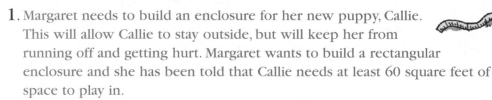

Part I: Stories to Inequalities

Use variables to write an inequality or set of inequalities that describes each of the following situations. Be sure to explain what your variables represent.

1. Margaret needs to build an enclosure for her new puppy, Callie. This will allow Callie to stay outside, but will keep her from running off and getting hurt. Margaret wants to build a rectangular enclosure and she has been told that Callie needs at least 60 square feet of space to play in.

   Margaret has to decide what dimensions to make the enclosure.

2. Lisa and Joel are a young couple furnishing a new house. They want to buy a computer, which will cost at least $1,500. (The exact cost depends on which special features they get.) Each is willing to contribute some money toward this purchase from their separate savings accounts.

   Joel's parents said they will contribute two dollars for every dollar that Joel contributes. Lisa's grandmother will exactly match Lisa's contribution.

   Joel and Lisa have to decide how much each of them will contribute to the computer purchase.

Part II: Inequalities to Stories

For each of the following inequalities, make up a real-world situation that the inequality describes. Again, be sure to explain what your variables represent.

3. $5x + 2y + 3z \leq 30$
4. $x^2 + y^2 \geq 81$

Homework 5   Group Reflection

People play many roles when they work in groups. Of course, this is not only true in math classes.

This assignment is an opportunity for you to reflect on the way you participate in groups. Be as thoughtful as possible when you answer these questions because they are designed to help you.

Note: You don't have to share this homework with anyone other than your teacher, unless you want to.

1. a. Try to remember a time when you were in a group and you or someone else was left out of a discussion. Describe the situation. Did anyone try to include that person? If not, why not? If so, then how?

    b. What might you have done to help with the situation?

2. a. What has been your experience when someone has made a mistake in your group?

    b. How do you think groups should handle mistakes by group members?

3. a. Try to remember a time when you thought of saying something, or you did not understand something, but were afraid to speak out. Describe the situation, what you wanted to say, and why you did not say it.

    b. How do you wish you had handled the situation?

4. Discuss how the amount of homework preparation you do for class affects your participation in group discussions.

Healthy Animals

Curtis is concerned about the diet he is feeding his pet. A nutritionist has recommended that the pet's diet include at least 30 grams of protein and 16 grams of fat per day.

Curtis has two types of foods available—Food A and Food B.

Each ounce of Food A supplies 2 grams of protein and 4 grams of fat, while each ounce of Food B supplies 6 grams of protein and 2 grams of fat. Curtis's pet should not eat a total of more than 12 ounces of food per day.

Curtis would like to vary the diet for his pet within these requirements, and needs to know what the choices are.

1. Choose variables to represent the amount of each type of food Curtis will include in the daily diet. State clearly what the variables represent.

2. Use your variables to write inequalities to describe the constraints of the situation.

Adapted from a problem on p. 292 of Lial and Miller, *Mathematics With Applications,* Scott, Foresman and Company, Glenview, Illinois, 1987.

Homework 6   Graphing Healthy Animals

Define the variables you used in *Healthy Animals* and state the constraints you found for that problem.

Then make a graph of each of your constraints. Graph each constraint on a separate set of axes. For each graph, be sure to label your axes and show their scales.

POW 2

Kick It!

The Free Thinkers Football League just has to be different. They aren't about to score their football games the way everyone else does. So they have thought up the following system:

- Each field goal counts for 5 points.
- Each touchdown counts for 3 points.

The only way to score points in their league is with field goals or touchdowns or some combination of them.

One of the Free Thinkers has noticed that not every score is possible in their league. A score of 1 point isn't possible, and neither is 2 or 4. She thinks that, beyond a certain number, all scores are possible. In fact, she thinks she knows the highest score that is impossible to make.

1. Figure out what that highest impossible score is for the Free Thinkers Football League. Then write why you are sure that all higher scores are possible.

2. Make up some other scoring systems (using whole numbers) and see whether there are scores that are impossible to make. Is there always a highest impossible score? If you think so, explain why. If you think there aren't always highest impossible scores, find a rule for when there are and when there are not.

3. In the situations where there is a highest impossible score, see if you can find any patterns or rules to use to figure out what the highest impossible score is. You may find patterns that apply in some special cases.

Write-up

1. *Problem statement:* State the problem clearly in your own words. Your problem statement should be clear enough so that someone unfamiliar with the problem can understand what you are being asked to do.

2. *Process:* Based on your notes, describe what you did in attempting to solve this problem. Include a description of any scoring systems you examined in addition to the one given in the problem.

3. *Conclusions:*

   a. State what you decided is the highest impossible score for the Free Thinkers' scoring system. Explain both why you think that score is impossible and why you think all higher scores are possible.

   b. Describe any results you got for other systems. Include any general ideas or patterns you found that apply to all scoring systems, and explain why they apply in general.

4. *Evaluation:* Discuss your personal reaction to this problem. For example, comment on the following:

   - Was this problem too hard or too easy?
   - Did you enjoy working on it?
   - Did you consider it educationally worthwhile?
   - How would you change the problem to make it better?

Picturing Cookies
—Part II

You have already worked with each of the constraints from the *Baker's Choice* problem on its own set of axes. Each graph gives you a picture of what that constraint means.

Now you need to see how to combine these constraints to get one picture of all of them together.

1. Begin with one of the constraints that you worked on before. Using a colored pencil, color the set of points that satisfy this constraint. *Note:* Unlike your work on *Picturing Pictures—Part I,* you should *not* color the points that do not satisfy the constraint.

2. Now choose a second constraint from the problem.

   a. On the *same set of axes,* but using a *different color,* color the set of points that satisfy this new constraint.

   b. Using your work so far, identify those points which satisfy *both* your new constraint and the constraint you used in Question 1.

3. Continue with the other constraints, using the same set of axes. Use a new color for each new constraint.

   a. Color the points that satisfy each new constraint.

   b. After graphing each new constraint, identify the points that satisfy all the constraints you have graphed so far.

4. When you have finished all the constraints, look at your overall work. Make a single new graph which shows the set of all points that represent possible combinations of the two types of cookies that the Woos can make.

   In your graph, show all the lines that come from the constraints, labeled with their equations.

   ▲ ▲ ▲ ▲ ▲ ▲ ▲ ▲

Homework 7

What's My Inequality

Graphs of inequalities can play an important role in understanding problem situations. So far in this unit, you have started with the inequality and found its graph. In this assignment, you go in the opposite direction.

For each graph below, find an inequality that represents the shaded area. (You should imagine that the shaded area continues indefinitely, including all points on the shaded side of the given line.)

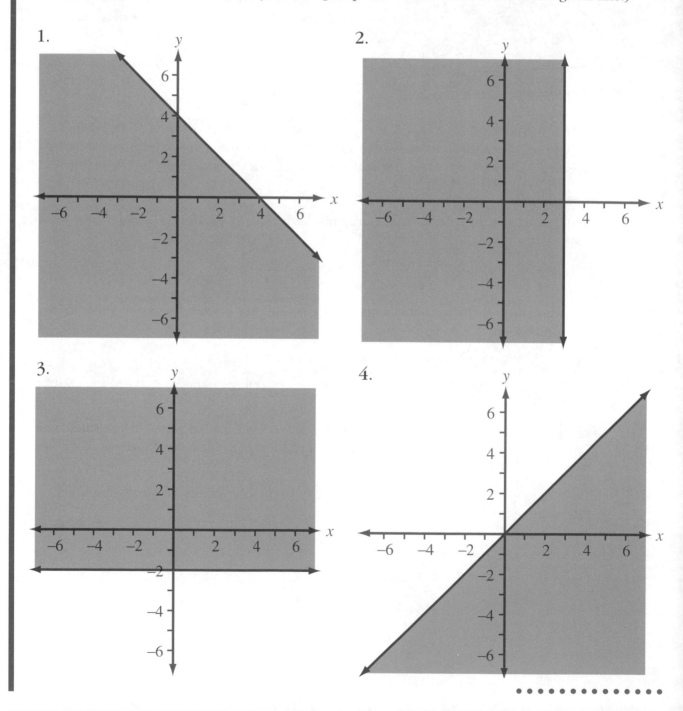

1.

2.

3.

4.

Feasible Diets

In *Homework 6: Graphing Healthy Animals,* you graphed the individual constraints from the problem *Healthy Animals.*

Now, your task is to draw the feasible region for that problem.

Here are the key facts from *Healthy Animals:*

• Curtis's pet needs at least 30 grams of protein.

• Curtis's pet needs at least 16 grams of fat.

• Each ounce of Food A supplies 2 grams of protein and 4 grams of fat.

• Each ounce of Food B supplies 6 grams of protein and 2 grams of fat.

• Curtis's pet should not eat a total of more than 12 ounces of food per day.

Be sure to identify your variables, label your axes, and show the scales on the axes.

Homework 8   Picturing Pictures

Hassan is an artist who specializes in geometric designs. He is trying to get ready for a street fair next month.

Hassan paints both watercolors and pastels. Each type of picture takes him about the same amount of time to paint. He figures he has time to make a total of at most 16 pictures.

The materials for each pastel will cost him $5 and the materials for each watercolor will cost him $15. He has $180 to spend on materials.

Hassan makes a profit of $40 on each pastel and a profit of $100 on each watercolor.

1. Use symbols to represent Hassan's constraints.

2. Make a graph that shows Hassan's feasible region; that is, the graph should show all the combinations of watercolors and pastels that satisfy his constraints.

3. For at least five points on your graph, find the profit that Hassan would make for that combination.

Profitable Pictures

Hassan asked his friend Sharma for advice about what combination of pictures to make.

She thought he should figure out a fair profit for that month's work, and then paint what he needed to achieve that profit.

Here are the facts you need from *Homework 8: Picturing Pictures:*

- Each pastel requires $5 in materials and earns a profit of $40 for Hassan.

- Each watercolor requires $15 in materials and earns a profit of $100 for Hassan.

- Hassan has $180 to spend on materials.

- Hassan can make at most 16 pictures.

See if you can help Hassan and Sharma. Turn in a written report on the situation. This report should include your work on Questions 1–4, but the most important part is your explanation on Question 5.

1. You have already found the feasible region for the problem, which is the set of points that satisfy the constraints. On graph paper, make a copy of this feasible region to use in this problem. Label your axes and show the scales.

2. Suppose Hassan decided $1000 would be a fair amount to make.

   a. Find three different combinations of watercolors and pastels that would make Hassan a profit of exactly $1000.

   b. Mark these three number pairs on your graph from Part 1.

3. Now, suppose Hassan wants to make only $500. Find three different combinations of watercolors and pastels that make Hassan a profit of exactly $500. *Using a different-colored pencil,* add those points to your graph.

4. Next, suppose that Hassan wants to make $600. Find three different combinations of watercolors and pastels that make Hassan a profit of exactly $600. *Using a different-colored pencil,* add those points to your graph.

5. Well, Hassan's mother has appeared on the scene and she thinks that he should try to earn as much as possible.

   Now, Hassan wants to figure out the most he can make within his constraints. He also wants to be able to prove to his mother that it is really the most. Please help Hassan with this problem.

   a. Find the maximum possible profit that Hassan can make and what combination of pictures he should make to earn that profit.

   b. Write an explanation that proves your answer is correct.

Homework 9   Curtis and Hassan Make Choices

1. Curtis goes into the pet store to buy a substantial supply of food for his pet. He sees that Food A costs $2 per pound and that Food B costs $3 per pound.

   Since he intends to vary his pet's diet from day to day anyway, he isn't especially concerned about how much he buys of each type of food.

   a. Suppose that Curtis has $30 to spend. Find several combinations of the two foods that he might buy, and plot them on an appropriately labeled graph.

   b. Now do the same thing assuming that Curtis spends $50, using the same set of axes.

   c. What do you notice about your answers to Questions 1a and 1b?

2. Hassan has a feeling that there's going to be a big demand for his work. He is considering changing his prices so that he makes a profit of $50 on each pastel and $175 on each watercolor.

   a. Based on these new profits for each type of picture, find some combinations of watercolors and pastels so that Hassan's total profit would be $700, and plot them on a graph.

   (The combinations you give here don't have to fit Hassan's usual constraints.)

   b. Now do the same for a total profit of $1750, using the same set of axes.

   c. What do you notice about your answers to Questions 2a and 2b?

Homework 10   You Are What You Eat

The Hernandez twins do not like breakfast. Given a choice, they would rather skip breakfast and concentrate on lunch.

When pressed, the only things they will eat for breakfast are Sugar Glops and Sweetums cereals. (The twins are allergic to milk, so they eat their cereal dry.)

Mr. Hernandez, on the other hand, has the strange idea that his children should eat breakfast every single morning. He also believes that their breakfast should be nutritious. Specifically, he would like each of them to get at least 5 grams of protein and not more than 50 grams of carbohydrate each morning.

The Sugar Glops package says that each ounce has 2 grams of protein and 15 grams of carbohydrate. The Sweetums box says that every ounce of Sweetums contains 1 gram of protein and 10 grams of carbohydrate.

So what is the least amount of cereal each twin can eat while satisfying their father's requirements? (Mr. Hernandez wants a proof that his criteria are met, and the twins want a proof that there is no way they can eat less.)

Homework 11   Changing What You Eat

In *Homework 10: You Are What You Eat,* the twins' solution was to just eat Sugar Glops.

That way, they could get their protein by eating only $2\frac{1}{2}$ ounces of cereal and still not get too many grams of carbohydrate.

But what if the cereals had been a little different from the way they were in that problem, or if Mr. Hernandez had been stricter about the twins' carbohydrates, or . . . ?

Here are some specific variations for you to think about.

1. Suppose that Sugar Glops is the same as in the original problem (with 2 grams of protein and 15 grams of carbohydrate per ounce), but that now Sweetums also has 2 grams of protein per ounce (and still has only 10 grams of carbohydrate per ounce).

   Also suppose that Mr. Hernandez still has a 50-gram limit on carbohydrate and still wants each of them to get at least 5 grams of protein.

   How much of each cereal should the twins eat if they want to eat as little cereal as possible?

2. Now suppose that Sugar Glops has 3 grams of protein and 20 grams of carbohydrate per ounce, and Sweetums is the same as in Problem 1 (2 grams of protein and 10 grams of carbohydrate per ounce).

   Also suppose that Mr. Hernandez has now decided that the twins can't eat more than 30 grams of carbohydrate (but they still need at least 5 grams of protein).

   What should the twins do?

3. Make up a variation on the problem where the twins would choose to eat just Sweetums.

4. Make up a variation on the problem where there would be no solution.

Rock 'n' Rap

The *Hits on a Shoestring* music company is trying to plan its next month's work. The company makes CDs of both rock and rap groups.

It costs them an average of $1500 to produce a rock CD and an average of $1200 to produce a rap CD. (The higher cost for rock comes from needing more instrumentalists for rock CDs.) It takes about 18 hours to produce a rock CD, while a rap CD takes 25 hours.

The company can afford to spend up to $15,000 on production next month. Also, according to the company's agreement with the employee union, the company must spend at least 175 hours on production.

Hits on a Shoestring makes $20,000 in profit on each rock CD they produce and $30,000 in profit on each rap CD they produce.

The company recently promised their distributor that they will not release more rap music than rock, because the distributor thinks the company is more closely associated with rock in the public mind.

1. Find out how many CDs they should make of each type next month to maximize their profit. (They can make a fraction of a CD next month and finish it the month after.)

2. Explain your process of arriving at an answer to Question 1 and the reason why you think your answer gives a maximum profit.

3. Suppose the profit situation is reversed and the company made $30,000 profit on each rock CD and $20,000 profit on each rap CD. Would this change your advice to them about how many to make of each type to maximize their profit? Explain your answer.

Homework 12   Getting on Good Terms

Graphing calculators can make it easier to find feasible regions, but in order to draw the graph of an equation on a graphing calculator, the equation needs to be put into "$y =$" form.

That is, you need to write the equation so that one variable is expressed in terms of the other. For example, you might rewrite the equation $y - 5 = 4x$ as $y = 4x + 5$.

1. For each of the equations below, express the variable y in terms of the variable x:

   a. $y - 2x = 7$

   b. $7y = 14x - 21$

   c. $5x + 3y = 17$

   d. $5(x + 3y) = 2x - 3$

2. To check that you haven't made a mistake on Question 1, do the following (and show your work):

   • For each equation in Part 1, choose two values for x and then use your answers to Question 1 to find the corresponding y-values.

   • Verify that each resulting pair of values for x and y satisfies the corresponding original equation.

For example, for the sample equation $y - 5 = 4x$, suppose you choose the values $x = 3$ and $x = -1$. The sample equation has been rewritten as $y = 4x + 5$, so you substitute the x-values into this equation, getting $y = 17$ when $x = 3$ and $y = 1$ when $x = -1$.

Then you substitute each of the pairs $(3, 17)$ and $(-1, 1)$ into the original equation, $y - 5 = 4x$, to check that they fit the equation. For example, you verify that $17 - 5 = 4 \cdot 3$ is a true statement.

Homework 13

The Big U

Big State University has to decide how many in-state students and how many out-of-state students to admit to its next class.

These conditions are constraints on their decision:

- The college president wants this class to contribute a total of at least $2,500,000 to the school after they graduate. In the past, Big State U has received an average of $8,000 in contributions from each in-state student admitted and an average of $2,000 from each out-of-state student admitted.

- The faculty at the college want entering students with good grade-point averages. Grades of in-state students average less than grades of out-of-state students. So the faculty are urging the school to admit at least as many out-of-state students as in-state students.

- The housing office is not willing to spend more than $85,000 to cover costs (such as meals and utilities) for students in dormitories during vacation periods. Since out-of-state students are more likely to stay on campus during vacations, the housing office needs to take these differences into account. In-state students will need an average of $100 each for vacation-time costs, while out-of-state students will need an average of $200 each.

- The college treasurer wants to minimize educational costs. Because students take different courses, it costs an average of $7,200 a year to teach an in-state student and an average of $6,000 a year to teach an out-of-state student.

Your job is to recommend how many students from each category should be admitted to Big State University, based on the constraints above. Include a proof that you are minimizing costs, showing any graphs that seem helpful, and explaining your reasoning carefully.

Adapted from *An Introduction to Mathematical Models in the Social and Life Sciences,* by Michael Olinick, Addison-Wesley, 1978, p. 169.

Baker's Choice Revisited

Abby and Bing Woo have a small bakery shop that specializes in cookies.

They make only two kinds of cookies—plain cookies and cookies with icing. They need to decide *how many dozens* of each kind of cookies to make for tomorrow.

One dozen of their *plain* cookies requires one pound of cookie dough (and no icing), while one dozen of their *iced* cookies requires 0.7 pounds of cookie dough and 0.4 pounds of icing.

The Woos know from experience that each dozen of the plain cookies requires about 0.1 hours of preparation time, and each dozen of the iced cookies requires about 0.15 hours of preparation time.

They also know that, no matter how many of each kind they make, they will be able to sell them all.

Their decision is limited by the following things:

- The ingredients they have on hand—they have 110 pounds of cookie dough and 32 pounds of icing.

- The amount of oven space available—they have room to bake a total of 140 dozen cookies for tomorrow.

- The amount of preparation time available—together they have 15 hours for cookie preparation.

Why should the Woos care how many cookies of each kind they make? You guessed it! They want to make as much money as possible. They sell the plain cookies for $6.00 a dozen and it costs them $4.50 a dozen to make those cookies. The iced cookies sell for $7.00 a dozen and cost $5.00 a dozen to make.

The Big Question is:

How many dozens of each kind of cookie should the Woos make so that their profit is as high as possible?

Your Assignment

Pretend that your group is a business consulting team. The Woos have come to you for help. Not only should you give them an answer, but you should explain to them clearly how you know that you have the best possible answer so that they will pick your group in the future when they need help.

You may want to review what you already know from earlier work on this problem. Look at your notes and earlier assignments.

Then write a report for the Woos. Your report should include the following:

- An answer to the Woos' dilemma, including a summary of how much cookie dough, icing, preparation time, and oven time they will use.

- An explanation for the Woos that will convince them that your answer gives them the most profit.

- Any graphs, charts, equations, or diagrams that are needed as part of your explanation.

You should write your report based on the assumption that the Woos do not know the techniques you have learned in this unit about solving this type of problem.

Homework 14   Reflections on Learning

Now that you are almost at the end of *Baker's Choice,* it's time
to reflect on your experience with this unit of mathematics.

1. How has your experience working on *Baker's Choice*
   been different from your previous experiences
   learning mathematics? Include differences in the way
   you learned as well as differences in the way the
   mathematics was presented.

2. Describe your own feelings about this type of
   learning. Include issues such as the following:

   • How well did you understand the mathematics?

   • How much did you enjoy the experience?

   • How did the experience affect your perceptions
     and attitudes about other students in the class?

Homework 15 Beginning Portfolio Selection

The main problem for this unit, *Baker's Choice,* is an example of a **linear programming** problem. You have seen several such problems, including the situations in the following activities:

- *Homework 8: Picturing Pictures*
- *Homework 10: You Are What You Eat*
- *Rock 'n' Rap*
- *Homework 13: The Big U*

1. Describe the steps you must go through to solve such a problem.

2. Pick three activities from the unit that helped you understand particular steps of this process. Explain how each activity helped you understand the process. (You do not need to restrict yourself to the activities listed above.)

Note: Selecting activities and writing the accompanying explanations are the first steps toward compiling your portfolio for this unit.

Baker's Choice Portfolio

Now that *Baker's Choice* is completed, it is time to put together your portfolio for the unit. This has three parts:

• Writing a cover letter summarizing the unit.

• Choosing papers to include from your work in this unit.

• Discussing your personal growth during the unit.

Cover Letter for Baker's Choice

Look back over *Baker's Choice* and describe the central problem of the unit and the main mathematical ideas. Your description should give an overview of how the key ideas were developed in this unit and how you used them to solve the central problem.

Selecting Papers from Baker's Choice

Your portfolio from *Baker's Choice* should contain the following items:

• *Homework 15: Beginning Portfolio Selection*

  Include the activities from the unit that you selected in *Homework 15: Beginning Portfolio Selection* along with your written work about those activities.

• A Problem of the Week

  Select one of the two POWs you completed during this unit (*The Broken Eggs* or *Kick It!*).

• Other quality work

  Select one or two other pieces of work that demonstrate your best efforts. (These can be any work from the unit—Problem of the Week, homework, classwork, presentation, and so on.)

• *Baker's Choice Revisited*

  Include your report from this problem.

• Later you will add the In-Class and Take-Home Assessments for *Baker's Choice*.

Personal Growth

Your cover letter for *Baker's Choice* describes how the unit develops. As part of your portfolio, write about your own development during this unit. You may want to address the following:

• How you feel you progressed in areas of:

  —working together with others

  —presenting to the class

  —writing about and describing your thought processes

• What you feel that you need to work on and how you might work on it.

You should include here any other thoughts about your experience with this unit that you want to share with a reader of your portfolio.

▲ ▲ ▲ ▲ ▲ ▲ ▲

In-Class Assessment for Baker's Choice

The problems in this assessment are variations on the *Baker's Choice* problem of the Woos. In each problem, you are to find the combination of plain and iced cookies that maximizes the Woos' profit for the new situation and explain your answer. Consider these three variations from the original situation *as three separate problems*.

Each problem is accompanied by a graph that shows the feasible region of the original problem, with the shaded area representing that original feasible region.

Problems 1 and 2 show a profit line based on the original problem. Problem 3 shows a profit line based on a different profit expression. The other lines shown in each case are the graphs of the equations corresponding to the original problem's constraint inequalities. These inequalities are as follows:

$$x + y \leq 140 \qquad \text{(for the amount of oven space)}$$

$$x + 0.7y \leq 110 \qquad \text{(for the amount of cookie dough)}$$

$$0.4y \leq 32 \qquad \text{(for the amount of icing)}$$

$$0.1x + 0.15y \leq 15 \qquad \text{(for the amount of the Woos'}$$
$$\text{preparation time)}$$

In-Class Assessment for Baker's Choice

1. Suppose everything is the same as the original problem, *except* that the Woos have an *unlimited amount of cookie dough*. What combination of plain and iced cookies should the Woos make to maximize their profit?

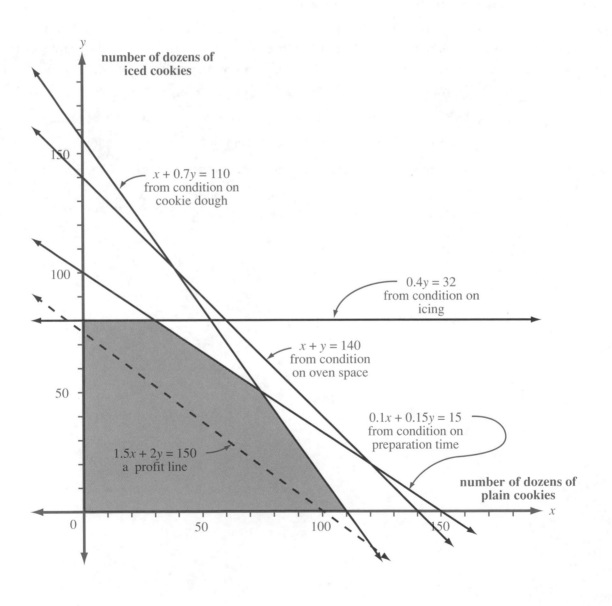

In-Class Assessment for Baker's Choice

2. Suppose everything is the same as the original problem, *except* that the Woos have the additional constraint that they can't sell more than 60 dozen plain cookies. What combination of plain and iced cookies should the Woos make to maximize their profit?

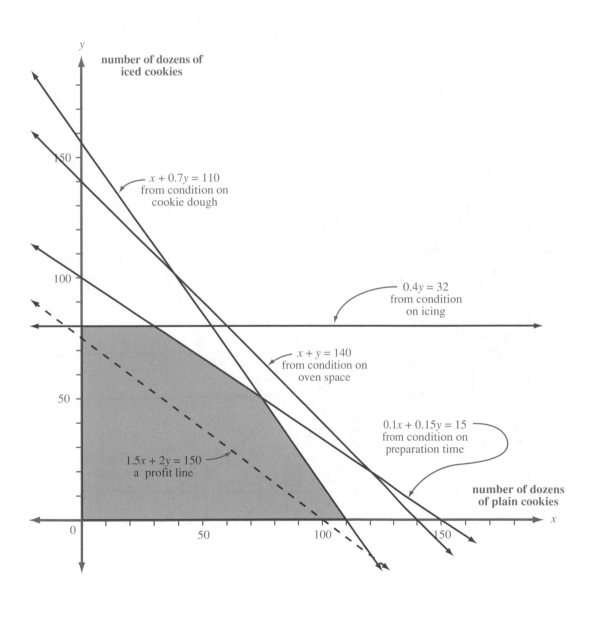

In-Class Assessment for Baker's Choice

3. Suppose everything is the same as the original problem, *except* that the Woos make a profit of $2 on each dozen plain cookies and $4 on each dozen iced cookies (instead of the original profits of $1.50 and $2). What combination of plain and iced cookies should the Woos make to maximize their profit?

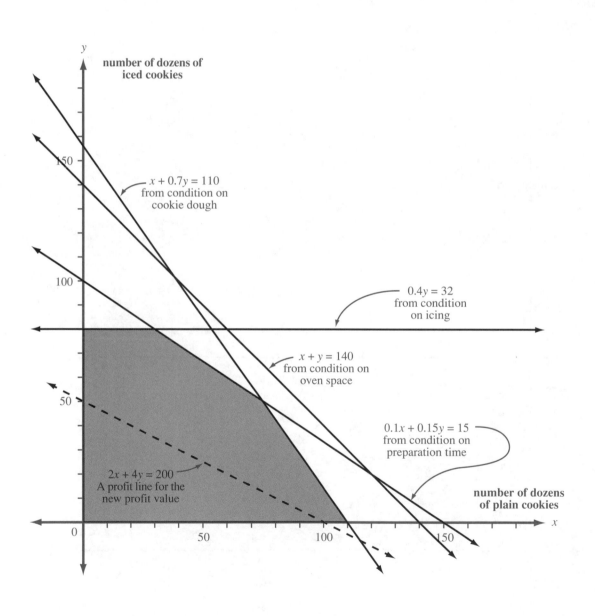

y

number of dozens of iced cookies

$x + 0.7y = 110$
from condition on cookie dough

$0.4y = 32$
from condition on icing

$x + y = 140$
from condition on oven space

$0.1x + 0.15y = 15$
from condition on preparation time

number of dozens of plain cookies

$2x + 4y = 200$
A profit line for the new profit value

x

Take-Home Assessment for *Baker's Choice*

Linda Sue is a stunt pilot, but she found that she can't make a living doing stunts. So she has bought a transport plane from her friend Philip. He agrees to help her set up her business.

He has two customers he no longer has time to serve and suggests that she work for them, delivering their merchandise.

Charley's Chicken Feed packages its product in containers that weigh 40 pounds and are 2 cubic feet in volume. Philip has been charging them $2.20 a container.

Careful Calculators packages its materials in cartons that weigh 50 pounds ans are 3 cubic feet in volume. Philip has been charging them $3.00 a carton.

The plane can hold a maximum volume of 2,000 cubic feet of cargo and it can carry a maximum weight of 37,000 pounds.

Both *Charley's Chicken Feed* and *Careful Calculators* told Linda that she can have as much business as she can handle, and the same flight route serves both customers' needs. Of course, Linda Sue wants to maximize the money she gets per flight, so she can spend more time on stunt flying.

Here are your tasks:

1. Use variables and algebra to describe the constraints on what Linda Sue can carry.

2. Sketch the feasible region for Linda Sue's situation.

3. Find the combination of chicken feed and calculators that Linda Sue should carry in order to maximize her income. (Assume that Linda Sue charges the same rates that Philip did.)

▼▼▼▼▼▼▼▼▼▼▼▼▼▼▼▼▼▼▼▼▼▼▼▼▼▼▼▼▼▼▼▼▼▼

More Broken Eggs

In *POW 1: The Broken Eggs,* you found a number of eggs that the farmer might possibly have had when her cart was knocked over.

You may have found only one solution to that problem, but there are actually many solutions.

Your task on this problem is to look for other solutions to the problem. Find as many as you can. If possible, find and describe a pattern for getting all the solutions and explain why all solutions fit your pattern.

Here are the facts you need to know:

• When the farmer put the eggs in groups of two, there was one egg left over.

• When she put them in groups of three, there was also one egg left over. The same thing happened when she put them in groups of four, five, or six.

• When she put the eggs in groups of seven, she ended up with complete groups of seven with no eggs left over.

▲▲▲▲▲▲▲

Hassan's a Hit!

Hassan's pictures are indeed a big hit, especially the watercolors. Based on his success, he is raising his prices as he planned in *Homework 9: Curtis and Hassan Make Choices.*

That is, he will now make a profit of $50 on each pastel and a profit of $175 on each watercolor.

Assume that he will still have the same constraints. That is, he will still have only $180 to spend on materials and will still be able to make at most 16 pictures.

He had already figured out, with the previous prices, how many he should make of each type of picture to maximize his overall profit.

If he still wants to maximize his overall profit, with the new prices, should he now change the number of pictures he makes of each type? Explain your answer.

▼▼▼▼▼▼▼▼▼▼▼▼▼▼▼▼▼▼▼▼▼▼▼▼▼▼▼▼▼▼▼▼▼

Get the Point?

In solving problems like the cookie problem, it is helpful to know how to find the point where two lines intersect.

Your group's goal in this activity is to discover a method of doing this, besides guessing or using graphs, by working with the equations of the two straight lines.

Your written report on the activity should include the following:

- Solutions to Questions 1a–1e.

- Two of the problems made up for Question 2 by individual group members, with solutions.

- Your group's written directions for Question 3.

1. For each of the following pairs of equations, find the point of intersection of their graphs by a method other than graphing or trial and error. When you think you have each solution, check it by graphing or by substituting the values into the pair of equations.

   a. $y = x$ and $3x = y + 4$

   b. $y = 2x + 5$ and $y = 3x - 7$

   c. $3x + 2y = 13$ and $y = 4x + 1$

   d. $7x - 3y = 31$ and $y - 5 = 3x$

   e. $x + 3y = 17$ and $2y + 1 = 3x$

2. Each person in the group should make up a pair of linear equations, and find the point of intersection. Then group members should trade problems (without giving solutions) and work on each other's problems, trying to find the point of intersection without guessing or graphing.

3. As a group, develop and write down general directions for finding the coordinates of the point of intersection of two equations for straight lines without guessing or graphing. Make your directions easy to follow, so someone in middle school could use them to "get the point."

▲▲▲▲▲▲▲

▼▼

A Charity Rock

At concerts given by the group *Rocking Pebbles,* some of the tickets are for reserved seats, and the rest are general admission.

For a recent *Rocking Pebbles* series of two weekend concerts, the *Pebbles* pledged to give half of the proceeds they got from the general admission tickets to charity. After the concerts, the charity called the *Pebbles'* manager to find out how much money the charity would get.

The manager looked up the records and found that, for the first night, 230 reserved seat tickets and 835 general admission tickets were sold. For the second night, 250 reserved seat tickets and 980 general admission tickets were sold. The manager saw that the total amount of money collected for tickets was $23,600 for the first night and $27,100 for the second night, but she didn't know the prices for the two different kinds of tickets. (The prices were the same at both concerts.)

Could you help the manager by figuring out how much the *Pebbles* will give to charity? While you're at it, figure out what the two ticket prices were.

▲▲▲▲▲▲▲▲

Producing Programming Problems

Your group is to make up a linear programming problem. The key ingredients you need to have in your problem are

- two variables,

- a ***linear expression*** using those variables to be maximized or minimized, and

- three or four ***linear constraints.***

Once you have written your problem, you must solve it.

Then you prepare an *interesting* 5 to 10 minute presentation with the overhead projector which

- explains the problem,

- provides a solution of the problem, and

- proves there is no better solution.

Photographic Credits

Assignment Photography
Hilary Turner

Classroom Photography
11 Capuchino High School, Chicha Lynch; **17** San Lorenzo Valley High School, Kim Gough; **28** Marshall High School, Maureen Burkhart; **35** San Lorenzo Valley High School, Kim Gough; **38** West High School, Janice Bussey; **47** Colton High School, Sharon Taylor; **54** Colton High School, Sharon Taylor; **56** Roosevelt High School, George Giffen; **67** Marshall High School, Maureen Burkhart; **81** Colton High School, Sharon Taylor; **86** Roosevelt High School, George Giffen; **95** Marshall High School, Maureen Burkhart; **102** Capuchino High School, Chicha Lynch; **108** Roosevelt High School, George Giffen; **118** Hilary Turner.